A2-Level
Physics

The Revision Guide

Exam Board: OCR A

Editors:
Amy Boutal, Sarah Hilton, Alan Rix, Julie Wakeling, Sarah Williams

Contributors
Peter Cecil, Mark A. Edwards, Barbara Mascetti, John Myers, Zoe Nye, Moira Steven, Andy Williams

Proofreaders:
Ian Francis, Glenn Rogers

Published by Coordination Group Publications Ltd.

ISBN: 978 1 84762 271 6

Groovy website: www.cgpbooks.co.uk
Jolly bits of clipart from CorelDRAW®
Printed by Elanders Hindson Ltd, Newcastle upon Tyne.

Based on the classic CGP style created by Richard Parsons.

Contents

The Scientific Process

'How Science Works' is all about the scientific process — how we develop and test scientific ideas.
It's what scientists do all day, every day (well, except at coffee time — never come between a scientist and their coffee).

Scientists Come Up with **Theories** — Then **Test Them**...

Science tries to explain **how** and **why** things happen — it **answers questions**. It's all about seeking and gaining **knowledge** about the world around us. Scientists do this by **asking** questions and **suggesting** answers and then **testing** them, to see if they're correct — this is the **scientific process**.

1) **Ask** a question — make an **observation** and ask **why or how** it happens.
   E.g. what is the nature of light?

2) **Suggest** an answer, or part of an answer, by forming:
   - a **theory** (a possible **explanation** of the observations)
     e.g. light is a wave.
   - a **model** (a **simplified picture** of what's physically going on)

3) Make a **prediction** or **hypothesis** — a **specific testable statement**, based on the theory, about what will happen in a test situation.
   E.g. light should interfere and diffract.

4) Carry out a **test** — to provide **evidence** that will support the prediction, or help disprove it. E.g. Young's double-slit experiment.

The evidence supported Quentin's Theory of Flammable Burps.

A theory is only scientific if it can be tested.

...Then They **Tell** Everyone About Their **Results**...

The results are **published** — scientists need to let others know about their work. Scientists publish their results in **scientific journals**. These are just like normal magazines, only they contain **scientific reports** (called papers) instead of the latest celebrity gossip.

1) Scientific reports are similar to the **lab write-ups** you do in school. And just as a lab write-up is **reviewed** (marked) by your teacher, reports in scientific journals undergo **peer review** before they're published.

2) The report is sent out to **peers** — other scientists that are experts in the **same area**. They examine the data and results, and if they think that the conclusion is reasonable it's **published**. This makes sure that work published in scientific journals is of a **good standard**.

3) But peer review **can't guarantee** the science is **correct** — other scientists still need to **reproduce** it.

4) Sometimes **mistakes** are made and bad work is published. Peer review **isn't perfect** but it's probably the best way for scientists to self-regulate their work and to publish **quality reports**.

...Then **Other Scientists** Will **Test** the Theory Too

Other scientists read the published theories and results, and try to **test the theory** themselves. This involves:
- Repeating the **exact same experiments**.
- Using the theory to make **new predictions** and then testing them with **new experiments**.

If the **Evidence** Supports a Theory, It's **Accepted** — *for Now*

1) If all the experiments in all the world provide evidence to back it up, the theory is thought of as **scientific 'fact'** (for now).

2) But they never become **totally undisputable** fact. Scientific **breakthroughs or advances** could provide new ways to question and test the theory, which could lead to **new evidence** that **conflicts** with the current evidence. Then the testing starts all over again...

And this, my friend, is the **tentative nature of scientific knowledge** — it's always **changing** and **evolving**.

The Scientific Process

So scientists need evidence to back up their theories. They get it by carrying out experiments, and when that's not possible they carry out studies. But why bother with science at all? We want to know as much as possible so we can use it to try and improve our lives (and because we're nosey).

Evidence Comes From Controlled Lab Experiments...

1) Results from **controlled experiments** in **laboratories** are **great**.

2) A lab is the easiest place to **control variables** so that they're all **kept constant** (except for the one you're investigating).

> For example, finding the specific heat capacity of a material by heating it and measuring the temperature change (see p. 18). All other variables need to be kept the same, e.g. the mass and shape of material you use and the external temperature, as they may also affect your results.

... That You can Draw Meaningful Conclusions From

1) You always need to make your experiments as **controlled** as possible so you can be confident that any effects you see are linked to the variable you're changing.

2) If you do find a relationship, you need to be careful what you conclude. You need to decide whether the effect you're seeing is **caused** by changing a variable, or whether the two are just **correlated**.

"Right Geoff, you can start the experiment now... I've stopped time..."

Society Makes Decisions Based on Scientific Evidence

1) Lots of scientific work eventually leads to **important discoveries** or breakthroughs that could **benefit humankind**.

2) These results are **used by society** (that's you, me and everyone else) to **make decisions** — about the way we live, what we eat, what we drive, etc.

3) All sections of society use scientific evidence to make decisions, e.g. politicians use it to devise policies and individuals use science to make decisions about their own lives.

Other factors can **influence** decisions about science or the way science is used:

Economic factors

- Society has to consider the **cost** of implementing changes based on scientific conclusions — e.g. the cost of reducing the UK's carbon emissions to limit the human contribution to **global warming**.

- Scientific research is often **expensive**. E.g. in areas such as astronomy, the Government has to **justify** spending money on a new telescope rather than pumping money into, say, the **NHS** or **schools**.

Social factors

- **Decisions** affect **people's lives** — e.g. when looking for a site to build a **nuclear power station**, you need to consider how it would affect the lives of the people in the **surrounding area**.

Environmental factors

- Many scientists suggest that building **wind farms** would be a **cheap** and **environmentally friendly** way to generate electricity in the future. But some people think that because **wind turbines** can **harm wildlife** such as birds and bats, other methods of generating electricity should be used.

So there you have it — how science works...

Hopefully these pages have given you a nice intro to how science works, e.g. what scientists do to provide you with 'facts'. You need to understand this, as you're expected to know how science works yourself — for the exam and for life.

Momentum and Impulse

We're going to kick off with a couple of pages about linear momentum — that's momentum in a straight line (not a circle or anything complicated like that). You'll have met momentum before so it shouldn't be too hard.

Understanding **Momentum** helps you do **Calculations** on **Collisions**

The **momentum** of an object depends on two things — its **mass** and **velocity**.
The **product** of these two values is the momentum of the object.

$$\text{momentum} = \text{mass} \times \text{velocity}$$

or in symbols:

$$p \ (\text{in kg ms}^{-1}) = m \ (\text{in kg}) \times v \ (\text{in ms}^{-1})$$

Hands up if you want to learn some physics.

Remember, momentum is a **vector quantity**, so just like velocity, it has size and direction.

Momentum is always **Conserved**

1)   Assuming **no external forces** act, momentum is always **conserved**.

2)   This means the **total momentum** of two objects **before** they collide **equals** the total momentum **after** the collision.

3)   This is really handy for working out the **velocity** of objects after a collision (as you do...):

> *Example*   A skater of mass 75 kg and velocity 4 ms⁻¹ collides with a stationary skater of mass 50 kg.
> The two skaters join together and move off in the same direction. Calculate their velocity after impact.
>
> 4ms⁻¹   0ms⁻¹   v = ?
> 75 kg   50 kg   125 kg
> BEFORE   AFTER
>
> *Before you start a momentum calculation, always draw a quick sketch.*
>
> Momentum of skaters before = Momentum of skaters after
> $$(75 \times 4) + (50 \times 0) = 125v$$
> $$300 = 125v$$
> $$\text{So } v = 2.4 \text{ ms}^{-1}$$

4)   The same principle can be applied in **explosions**. E.g. if you fire an **air rifle**, the **forward momentum** gained by the pellet **equals** the **backward momentum** of the rifle, and you feel the rifle recoiling into your shoulder.

> *Example*   A bullet of mass 0.005 kg is shot from a rifle at a speed of 200 ms⁻¹.
> The rifle has a mass of 4 kg. Calculate the velocity at which the rifle recoils.
>
> 4 kg x v   0.005 kg x 200 ms⁻¹
>
> Momentum before explosion = Momentum after explosion
> $$0 = (0.005 \times 200) + (4 \times v)$$
> $$0 = 1 + 4v$$
> $$v = -0.25 \text{ ms}^{-1}$$

5)   In reality, collisions and explosions usually happen in more than one dimension.
Don't worry though — you'll only be given problems to solve in **one dimension**.

Momentum and Impulse

Collisions can be Elastic or Inelastic

An **elastic collision** is one where **momentum** is **conserved** and **kinetic energy** is **conserved** — i.e. no energy is dissipated as heat, sound, etc. If a collision is **inelastic** it means that some of the kinetic energy is converted into other forms during the collision. But **momentum is always conserved.**

Example A toy lorry (mass 2 kg) travelling at 3 ms⁻¹ crashes into a smaller toy car (mass 800 g), travelling in the same direction at 2 ms⁻¹. The velocity of the lorry after the collision is 2.6 ms⁻¹ in the same direction. Calculate the new velocity of the car and the total kinetic energy before and after the collision.

2kg
3ms⁻¹

800g
2ms⁻¹

$v = 2.6ms^{-1}$ $v = ?$

BEFORE

AFTER

Momentum before collision = Momentum after collision

$(2 \times 3) + (0.8 \times 2) = (2 \times 2.6) + (0.8v)$

$7.6 = 5.2 + 0.8v$

$2.4 = 0.8v$

$v = 3\ ms^{-1}$

The difference in the two values is the amount of kinetic energy <u>dissipated</u> as heat or sound, or in damaging the vehicles — so this is an <u>inelastic collision</u>.

Kinetic Energy before = KE of lorry + KE of car

$= \frac{1}{2}mv^2$ (lorry) + $\frac{1}{2}mv^2$ (car)

$= \frac{1}{2}(2 \times 3^2) + \frac{1}{2}(0.8 \times 2^2)$

$= 9 + 1.6$

$= 10.6\ J$

Kinetic Energy after = $\frac{1}{2}(2 \times 2.6^2) + \frac{1}{2}(0.8 \times 3^2)$

$= 6.76 + 3.6$

$= 10.36\ J$

Impulse = Change in Momentum

1) Newton's second law says **force = rate of change of momentum** (see page 6), or $F = (mv - mu) \div t$

2) **Rearranging** Newton's 2nd law gives: **Impulse** is defined as **average force × time**, *Ft*. The units of impulse are **newton seconds**, Ns.

$$Ft = mv - mu$$
(where *v* is the final velocity and *u* is the initial velocity)

so ***impulse − change of momentum***

Impulse is the area under a force-time graph.

3) So, the **force** of an impact can be **reduced** by **increasing the time** of the impact.

For example, a toy car with a mass of 1 kg, travelling at 5 ms⁻¹, hits a wall and stops in a time of 0.5 seconds.

The average force on the car is: $F = \dfrac{mv - mu}{t} = \dfrac{(1 \times 5) - (1 \times 0)}{0.5} = 10\ N$

But if the time of impact is doubled to 1 second, the force on the car is halved.

This is the idea behind car crumple zones which increase the time of an impact to reduce the force on the passengers.

Practice Questions

Q1 Give two examples of conservation of momentum in practice.

Q2 Describe what happens when a tiny object makes an elastic collision with a massive object, and why.

Exam Questions

Q1 A ball of mass 0.6 kg moving at 5 ms⁻¹ collides with a larger stationary ball of mass 2 kg. The smaller ball rebounds in the opposite direction at 2.4 ms⁻¹.
(a) What is the velocity of the larger ball immediately after the collision? [3 marks]
(b) Is this an elastic or inelastic collision? Explain your answer. [3 marks]

Q2 A toy train of mass 0.7 kg, travelling at 0.3 ms⁻¹, collides with a stationary toy carriage of mass 0.4 kg. The two toys couple together. What is their new velocity? [3 marks]

Momentum will never be an endangered species — it's always conserved...

*It seems a bit of a contradiction to say that momentum's always conserved then tell you that impulse is the change in momentum. The difference is that impulse is only talking about the change of momentum of one of the objects, whereas conservation of momentum is talking about the **whole** system.*

Newton's Laws of Motion

You did most of this at GCSE, but that doesn't mean you can just skip over it now. You'll be kicking yourself if you forget this stuff in the exam — easy marks...

Newton's **1st Law** says that a **Force** is Needed to Change Velocity

1) **Newton's 1st law of motion** states the **velocity** of an object will **not change** unless a **resultant force** acts on it.

2) In plain English this means a body will remain at rest or moving in a **straight line** at a **constant speed**, unless acted on by a **resultant force**.

 An apple sitting on a table won't go anywhere because the **forces** on it are **balanced**.

reaction (R) = **weight** (mg)

(force of table pushing apple up) (force of gravity pulling apple down)

3) If the forces **aren't balanced**, the **overall resultant force** will cause the body to **accelerate** — if you gave the apple above a shove, there'd be a resultant force acting on it and it would roll off the table. Acceleration can mean a change in **direction**, or **speed**, or both. (See Newton's 2nd law, below.)

Newton's **2nd Law** says that Force is the **Rate of Change in Momentum**...

*"The **rate of change of momentum** of an object is **directly proportional** to the **resultant force** which acts on the object."* so $F = \dfrac{\Delta mv}{\Delta t}$

If mass is constant, this can be written as the well-known equation:

resultant force (F) = mass (m) × acceleration (a)

Learn this — it crops up all over the place in A2 Physics.
And learn what it means too:

1) It says that the **more force** you have acting on a certain mass, the **more acceleration** you get.

2) It says that for a given force the **more mass** you have, the **less acceleration** you get.

REMEMBER:
1) The **resultant force** is the **vector sum** of all the forces.
2) The force is **always** measured in **newtons**. Always.
3) The **mass** is always measured in **kilograms**.
4) **a** is the **acceleration** of the object as a result of F. It's **always** measured in **metres per second per second (ms⁻²)**.
5) The **acceleration** is always in the **same direction** as the **resultant force**.

F = ma is a Special Case of Newton's 2nd Law

Newton's 2nd law says that if the **mass** of an object is **constant**, then the **bigger** the force acting on it, the **greater** its **acceleration** — i.e. **F = ma**. But, if the **mass** of the object is **changing** — e.g. if it is accelerating at close to the **speed of light** — then you **can't** use **F = ma**.

Don't worry though — **Newton's 2nd law still applies**, it's just that the 'rate of **change of momentum**' bit refers to a **change in mass** and velocity.

Daisy was always being told that she was a special case.

Newton's Laws of Motion

Newton's **3rd Law** says each Force has an **Equal**, **Opposite Reaction Force**

There are a few different ways of stating Newton's 3rd law, but the clearest way is:

> **If an object A EXERTS a FORCE on object B, then
> object B exerts AN EQUAL BUT OPPOSITE FORCE on object A.**

You'll also hear the law as "every action has an equal and opposite reaction". But this confuses people who wrongly think the forces are both applied to the same object. (If that were the case, you'd get a resultant force of zero and nothing would ever move anywhere...)

The two forces actually represent the **same interaction**, just seen from two **different perspectives**:

1) If you **push against a wall**, the wall will **push back** against you, **just as hard**. As soon as you stop pushing, so does the wall. Amazing...

2) If you **pull a cart**, whatever force **you exert** on the rope, the rope exerts the **exact opposite** pull on you.

3) When you go **swimming**, you push **back** against the water with your arms and legs, and the water pushes you **forwards** with an equal-sized force.

This looks like Newton's 3rd law...

Gravity pulls down on book

But it's <u>NOT</u>.

Table pushes upwards on book

...because both forces are acting on the book, and they're not of the same type. This is two separate interactions. The forces are equal and opposite, resulting in zero acceleration, so this is showing Newton's 1st law.

Newton's 3rd law applies in **all situations** and to all **types of force**. But the pairs of forces are always the **same type**, e.g. both gravitational or both electrical.

Newton's 3rd law is a consequence of the **conservation of momentum** (page 4). A **resultant force** acting means a change in **mass** or **acceleration** ($F = ma$) — which means a **change in momentum**. Momentum is always **conserved**, so whenever one object exerts a force on another (and changes its momentum) the second object must exert an equal-sized force back onto the first object so that the overall change in momentum is zero.

Practice Questions

Q1 State Newton's 1st, 2nd and 3rd laws of motion, and explain what they mean.

Q2 Give an example of a situation where you couldn't use F = ma. Why wouldn't the equation apply?

Q3 Sketch a force diagram of a book resting on a table to illustrate Newton's 3rd law.

Exam Questions

Q1 A parachutist with a mass of 78 kg jumps out of a plane. As she falls, the resultant force acting on her changes.
   (a) Use Newton's 2nd law to explain why she initially accelerates. [2 marks]
   (b) What is the initial vertical force on the parachutist? Use $g = 9.81$ ms^{-2}. [1 mark]
   (c) After a time, the parachutist reaches terminal velocity and stops accelerating.
       Use Newton's 1st law to explain why the resultant force on the parachutist is zero at this point. [2 marks]

Q2 A boat is moving across a river. The engines provide a force of 500 N at right angles to the flow of the river, and the boat experiences a drag of 100 N in the opposite direction. The force on the boat due to the flow of the river is 300 N. The mass of the boat is 250 kg. Calculate the magnitude of the acceleration of the boat. [4 marks]

<u>Newton's three incredibly important laws of motion...</u>

These equations may not really fill you with a huge amount of excitement (and I hardly blame you if they don't)... but it was pretty fantastic at the time — suddenly people actually understood how forces work, and how they affect motion. I mean arguably it was one of the most important scientific discoveries ever...

Circular Motion

*It's probably worth putting a bookmark in here — this stuff is needed **all over** the place.*

Angles can be Expressed in Radians

The angle in **radians**, θ, is defined as the **arc-length** divided by the radius of the circle.

For a **complete circle** (360°), the arc-length is just the circumference of the circle ($2\pi r$). Dividing this by the radius (r) gives 2π. So there are 2π radians in a complete circle.

Some common angles:

45°
$\dfrac{\pi}{4}$ rad

90°
$\dfrac{\pi}{2}$ rad

180°
π rad

angle in radians $= \dfrac{2\pi}{360} \times$ angle in degrees

1 radian is about 57°

The **Angular Speed** is the **Angle** an Object Rotates Through **per Second**

1) Just as **linear speed**, v, is defined as distance ÷ time, the **angular speed**, ω, is defined as **angle ÷ time**. The unit is rad s^{-1} — radians per second.

$$\omega = \frac{\theta}{t}$$

ω = angular speed (rad s^{-1}) — the symbol for angular speed is the little Greek 'omega', not a w.
θ = angle (radians) turned through in a time, t (seconds)

2) The **linear speed**, v, and **angular speed**, ω, of a rotating object are linked by the equation:

$$v = r\omega$$

v = linear speed (ms^{-1}), r = radius of the circle (m),
ω = angular speed (rad s^{-1})

Example   **Beam** of **Particles** in a **Cyclotron** *(a type of particle accelerator)*

FAST

SLOW

All parts of the beam take the same time to rotate through this angle.

1) Different parts of the particle beam are rotating at **different linear speeds**, v. (The linear speed is sometimes called **tangential velocity**.)

2) But all the parts **rotate** through the **same angle** in the **same time** — so they have the **same angular speed**.

Circular Motion has a **Frequency** and **Period**

1) The frequency, f, is the number of complete **revolutions per second** (rev s^{-1} or hertz, Hz).

2) The period, T, is the **time taken** for a complete revolution (in seconds).

3) Frequency and period are **linked** by the equation:

$$f = \frac{1}{T}$$

f = frequency in rev s^{-1}, T = period in s

4) For a complete circle, an object turns through 2π radians in a time T, so frequency and period are related to ω by:

$$\omega = 2\pi f \quad \text{and} \quad \omega = \frac{2\pi}{T}$$

f = frequency in rev s^{-1}, T = period in s, ω = angular speed in rad s^{-1}

Circular Motion

Objects Travelling in Circles are **Accelerating** since their **Velocity is Changing**

FRICTION FORCE

1) Even if the car shown is going at a **constant speed**, its **velocity** is changing since its **direction** is changing.

2) Since acceleration is defined as the **rate of change of velocity**, the car is accelerating even though it isn't going any faster.

3) This acceleration is called the **centripetal acceleration** and is always directed towards the **centre of the circle**.

There are two formulas for centripetal acceleration:

$$a = \frac{v^2}{r} \quad \text{and} \quad a = \omega^2 r$$

a = centripetal acceleration in ms^{-2}
v = linear speed in ms^{-1}
ω = angular speed in rad s^{-1}
r = radius in m

The **Centripetal Acceleration** is produced by a **Centripetal Force**

From Newton's laws, if there's a **centripetal acceleration**, there must be a **centripetal force** acting towards the **centre of the circle**.

Since **F** = **ma**, the centripetal force must be:

$$F = \frac{mv^2}{r} \quad \text{and} \quad F = m\omega^2 r$$

The centripetal force is what keeps the object moving in a circle — remove the force and the object would fly off at a tangent.

Men cowered from the force of the centripede.

Practice Questions

Q1 How many radians are there in a complete circle?
Q2 How is angular speed defined and what is the relationship between angular speed and linear speed?
Q3 Define the period and frequency of circular motion. What is the relationship between period and angular speed?
Q4 In which direction does the centripetal force act, and what happens when this force is removed?

Exam Questions

Q1 (a) At what angular speed does the Earth orbit the Sun? (1 year = 3.2×10^7 s) [2 marks]

(b) Calculate the Earth's linear speed. (Assume radius of orbit = 1.5×10^{11} m) [2 marks]

(c) Calculate the centripetal force needed to keep the Earth in its orbit. (Mass of Earth = 6.0×10^{24} kg) [2 marks]

(d) What is providing this force? [1 mark]

Q2 A bucket full of water, tied to a rope, is being swung around in a vertical circle (so it is upside down at the top of the swing). The radius of the circle is 1 m.

(a) By considering the acceleration due to gravity at the top of the swing, what is the minimum frequency with which the bucket can be swung without any water falling out? [3 marks]

(b) The bucket is now swung with a constant angular speed of 5 rad s^{-1}. What will be the tension in the rope when the bucket is at the top of the swing if the total mass of the bucket and water is 10 kg? [2 marks]

I'm spinnin' around, move out of my way...

*"Centripetal" just means "centre-seeking". The centripetal force is what actually causes circular motion. What you **feel** when you're spinning, though, is the reaction (centrifugal) force. Don't get the two mixed up.*

Gravitational Fields

*Gravity's all about masses **attracting** each other. If the Earth didn't have a **gravitational field,** apples wouldn't fall to the ground and you'd probably be floating off into space instead of sitting here reading this page...*

Masses in a **Gravitational Field** Experience a **Force of Attraction**

1) Any object with mass will **experience an attractive force** if you put it in the **gravitational field** of another object.

2) Only objects with a **large** mass, such as stars and planets, have a significant effect. E.g. the gravitational fields of the **Moon** and the **Sun** are noticeable here on Earth — they're the main cause of our **tides**.

You can **Calculate Forces** Using **Newton's Law of Gravitation**

1) The **force** experienced by an object in a gravitational field is always **attractive**. It's a **vector** which depends on the **masses** involved and the **distance** between them.

2) The diagram shows the force acting on mass **m** due to mass **M**. (The force on **M** due to **m** is equal but in the opposite direction.)

3) **M** and **m** are uniform spheres, which behave as **point masses** — as if all their mass is concentrated at the centre.

4) It's easy to work out the **force** experienced by a **point mass** in a **gravitational field** — you just put the numbers into this **equation**:

NEWTON'S LAW OF GRAVITATION:

$$F = -\frac{GMm}{r^2}$$

The negative sign shows that the vector **F** is in the opposite direction to **r** (displacement of **m** from **M**).

where **F** is the force acting on mass **m** due to mass **M**,
M and **m** behave as point masses,
G is the **gravitational constant** — 6.67×10^{-11} Nm^2kg^{-2}.
r is the distance (in metres) between the centres of the two masses.

It doesn't matter what you call the masses, M and m, m_1 and m_2, Paul and Larry...

Newton's Law of Gravitation is an **Inverse Square Law**

The law of gravitation is an **inverse square law** $\left(F \propto \dfrac{1}{r^2} \right)$ so:

1) if the distance **r** between the masses **increases** then the force **F** will **decrease**.

2) if the **distance doubles**, the **force** will be one **quarter** the strength of the original force.

The officers weren't sure how to enforce the inverse square law.

You can Draw **Lines of Force** to Show the **Field** Around an Object

Gravitational lines of force (or "field lines") are **arrows** showing the **direction of the force** that masses would feel in a gravitational field.

1) If you put a small mass, **m**, anywhere in the Earth's gravitational field, it will always be attracted **towards** the Earth.

2) The Earth's gravitational field is **radial** — the lines of force meet at the centre of the Earth.

3) If you move mass **m** further away from the Earth — where the **lines** of force are **further apart** — the **force** it experiences **decreases**.

4) The small mass, **m**, has a gravitational field of its own. This doesn't have a noticeable effect on the Earth though, because the Earth is so much **more massive**.

5) Close to the Earth's surface, the gravitational field is (almost) uniform — so the **field lines** are (almost) **parallel**. You can usually **assume** that the field is perfectly uniform.

Gravitational Fields

The **Field Strength** is the **Force per Unit Mass**

Gravitational field strength, **g**, is the **force per unit mass**. Its value depends on **where you are** in the field. There's a really simple equation for working it out:

$$g = \frac{F}{m}$$

g has units of newtons per kilogram (Nkg⁻¹)

Murray loved showing off his field strength.

1) **F** is the force experienced by a mass **m** when it's placed in the gravitational field. Divide **F** by **m** and you get the **force per unit mass**.

2) **g** is a **vector** quantity, always pointing towards the centre of the mass whose field you're describing.

3) Since the gravitational field is almost uniform at the Earth's surface, you can assume **g** is a constant.

4) **g** is just the **acceleration** of a mass in a gravitational field. It's often called the **acceleration due to gravity**.

The **value** of **g** at the **Earth's surface** is approximately **9.81 ms⁻²** (or 9.81 Nkg⁻¹).

In a **Radial Field**, **g** is **Inversely Proportional** to r^2

Point masses have **radial** gravitational fields. The value of **g** depends on the distance **r** from the centre of the point mass **M**...

$$g = -\frac{GM}{r^2}$$

The graph shows how **g** varies for the Earth. R_E is the Earth's radius

And it's an **inverse square law** again — as **r** increases, **g** decreases.

Example   The graph shows how the gravitational field strength, **g**, varies with distance, **r**, from the centre of the planet Mars. The radius of Mars is approximately 3.4 × 10³ km. Estimate the mass of Mars.

You can see from the graph that the value of **g** at the surface of Mars is about 3.7 Nkg⁻¹.

Rearrange the formula: $g = -\dfrac{GM}{r^2}$ to find **M**, then stick the values in — don't forget to convert to standard units first. So, $M = \dfrac{gr^2}{G} = \dfrac{3.7 \times \left(3.4 \times 10^6\right)^2}{6.67 \times 10^{-11}} = $ **6.41 × 10²³ kg**.

Practice Questions

Q1   Write down Newton's law of gravitation.

Q2   Draw a diagram showing the Earth's gravitational field close to its surface.

Exam Questions

Q1   The Earth's radius is approximately 6400 km. Estimate its mass (use g = 9.81 Nkg⁻¹ at the Earth's surface).   [2 marks]

Q2   The Moon has a mass of 7.35 × 10²² kg and a radius of 1740 km.
   (a) Calculate the value of **g** at the Moon's surface.   [1 mark]
   (b) Calculate the gravitational force on a 25 kg object 10 m above the surface of the Moon.   [2 marks]

If you're really stuck, put 'Inverse Square Law'...

Clever chap, Newton, but famously tetchy. He got into fights with other physicists, mainly over planetary motion and calculus... the usual playground squabbles. Then he spent the rest of his life trying to turn scrap metal into gold. Weird.

Motion of Masses in Gravitational Fields

*Planets just go round and round in circles. Well, **ellipses** really, but I won't tell if you don't...*

Planets are Satellites which Orbit the Sun

1) A **satellite** is just any **smaller mass** which **orbits** a **much larger mass** — the **Moon** is a satellite of the Earth.

2) In our Solar System, the planets have **nearly circular orbits**... **so** you can use the **equations of circular motion**.

The Speed of an Orbit depends on its Radius and the Mass of the Larger Body

1) Earth feels a force due to the gravitational 'pull' of the **Sun**. This force is given by Newton's law of gravitation...

$$F = -\frac{GMm}{r^2}$$ (see p. 10)

2) The Earth has velocity **v**. Its linear speed is constant but its **direction** is not — so it's accelerating. The **centripetal force** causing this acceleration is:

$$F = \frac{mv^2}{r}$$

2) The **centripetal force** on the Earth must be a result of the **gravitational force** due to the Sun, and so these forces must be **equal**...

$$\frac{mv^2}{r} = \frac{GMm}{r^2}$$ and rearranging... $$v = \sqrt{\frac{GM}{r}}$$

... and the Period does too

The **time** taken **for one orbit** is called the **period**, **T**. For circular motion, $T = \frac{2\pi r}{v}$.

Substitute for **v** and rearrange... $$T^2 = \left(\frac{4\pi^2}{GM}\right)r^3$$

Example

The Moon takes 27.3 days to orbit the Earth. Calculate its distance from the Earth.
Take the mass of the Earth to be 5.975×10^{24} kg.

You're trying to find the radius of the orbit, **r**. Use the formula for period, **T**:

$$T^2 = \left(\frac{4\pi^2}{GM}\right)r^3$$

You've been given the values of **T** (27.3 days) and **M**, and you'll be able to look up the value of **G** on the exam data sheet — $G = 6.67 \times 10^{-11}$ Nm²kg⁻².

and rearrange it for **r³**: $$r^3 = \frac{T^2 GM}{4\pi^2}$$

and put the numbers in (convert to SI units first): $$r^3 = \frac{\left(2.36 \times 10^6\right)^2 \times \left(6.67 \times 10^{-11}\right) \times \left(5.975 \times 10^{24}\right)}{4\pi^2} = 5.62 \times 10^{25}$$

T = 27.3 days = 2.36×10^6 s
G = 6.67×10^{-11} Nm²kg⁻²
M = 5.975×10^{24} kg

$r = 3.83 \times 10^8$ m

$= \underline{\textbf{3.83} \times \textbf{10}^5 \textbf{ km}}$ (this is the distance between the centre of the Earth and the centre of the Moon)

Motion of Masses in Gravitational Fields

Geostationary Satellites *Orbit the Earth once in 24 hours*

1) Geostationary satellites orbit directly over the **equator** and are **always above the same point** on Earth.
2) A geostationary satellite travels at the **same angular speed as the Earth** turns below it.
3) These satellites are really useful for sending TV and telephone signals — the satellite is **stationary** relative to a certain point on the **Earth**, so you don't have to alter the angle of your receiver (or transmitter) to keep up.
4) Their orbit takes exactly **one day**.

Kepler's Laws *are about the Motion of Planets in the Solar System*

Kepler came up with these three laws around 1600, about 80 years before Newton developed his law of gravitation:

1) Each planet moves in an **ellipse** around the Sun (a circle is just a special kind of ellipse).
2) A line joining the Sun to a planet will sweep out **equal areas in equal times**.
   (Don't worry, you don't need to know about that one.)
3) The **period** of the orbit and the **mean distance** between the Sun and the planet are related by **Kepler's third law**:

$$T^2 \propto r^3$$

For circular motion, where r = radius of the orbit, $\dfrac{r^3}{T^2} = \text{constant} = \dfrac{GM}{4\pi^2}$.

It's either gravity or a giant white rabbit that makes the Earth orbit the Sun. I know which one I believe...

Example The diagram shows the orbits of two of Jupiter's moons, Io and Europa. The moon Io completes one orbit of Jupiter in 42.5 hours. Estimate the orbital period of Europa to the nearest hour, assuming both orbits are circular.

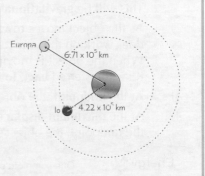

Europa 6.71×10^5 km
Io 4.22×10^5 km

Using Kepler's third law: $\dfrac{T_{Io}^{\,2}}{r_{Io}^{\,3}} = \dfrac{T_{Europa}^{\,2}}{r_{Europa}^{\,3}}$,

so $T_{Europa} = \sqrt{\dfrac{T_{Io}^{\,2}\, r_{Europa}^{\,3}}{r_{Io}^{\,3}}} = \sqrt{\dfrac{(42.5)^2 \times (6.71 \times 10^5)^3}{(4.22 \times 10^5)^3}} = 85$ hours (to the nearest hour).

Practice Questions

Q1 Derive an expression for the radius of the orbit of a planet around the Sun, in terms of the period of its orbit.

Q2 The International Space Station orbits the Earth with velocity v. If another vehicle docks with it, increasing its mass, what difference, if any, does this make to the speed or radius of the orbit?

Q3 Would a geostationary satellite be useful for making observations for weather forecasts? Give reasons.

Exam Questions

(Use $G = 6.67 \times 10^{-11}\,Nm^2kg^{-2}$, mass of Earth = 5.98×10^{24} kg, radius of Earth = 6400 km)

Q1 (a) A satellite orbits 200 km above the Earth's surface. Calculate the period of the satellite's orbit. [2 marks]
    (b) What is the linear speed of the satellite? [1 mark]

Q2 At what height above the Earth's surface would a geostationary satellite orbit? [3 marks]

Q3 The Sun has a mass of 2.0×10^{30} kg, but loses mass at a rate of around 6×10^9 kgs^{-1}.
Discuss whether this will have had any significant effect on the Earth's orbit over the past 50 000 years. [2 marks]

No fluffy bunnies were harmed in the making of these pages...

Kepler is sometimes proclaimed as the first science fiction writer. He wrote a tale about a fantastic trip to the Moon, where the book narrator's mum asks a demon the secret of space travel, to boldly go where — oh wait, different story. Unfortunately Kepler's book might have sparked the actual witchhunt on Kepler's mum, whoops-a-daisy...

Simple Harmonic Motion

Something simple at last, I like the sound of this. And colourful graphs too — you're in for a treat here.

SHM is Defined in terms of Acceleration and Displacement

1) An object moving with **simple harmonic motion** (SHM) **oscillates** to and fro, either side of a **midpoint**.

2) **Pendulums** and **mass-spring systems** (a mass hanging on a spring that's free to move up and down) are two examples.

3) The distance of the object from the midpoint is called its **displacement**.

4) There is always a **restoring force** pulling or pushing the object back **towards** the **midpoint**.

5) The **size** of the **restoring force** depends on the **displacement**, and the force makes the object **accelerate** towards the midpoint:

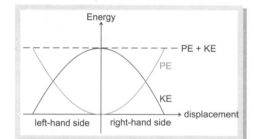

> **SHM:** an oscillation in which the **acceleration** of an object is **directly proportional** to its **displacement** from the **midpoint**, and is directed **towards the midpoint**.

The Restoring Force makes the Object Exchange PE and KE

1) The **type** of **potential energy** (PE) depends on **what it is** that's providing the **restoring force**. This will be **gravitational PE** for pendulums and **elastic PE** (elastic stored energy) for masses on springs.

2) As the object moves **towards the midpoint**, the restoring force **does work** on the object and so **transfers** some PE to KE. When the object is moving **away from the midpoint**, all that KE is transferred **back to PE** again.

3) At the **midpoint**, the object's **PE** is **zero** and its **KE** is **maximum**.

4) At the **maximum displacement** (the **amplitude**) on both sides of the midpoint, the object's **KE** is **zero** and its **PE** is **maximum**.

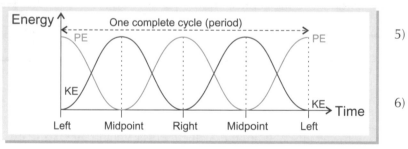

5) The **sum** of the **potential** and **kinetic** energy is called the **mechanical energy** and **stays constant** (as long as the motion isn't damped — see p. 16-17).

6) The **energy transfer** for one complete cycle of oscillation (see graph) is: PE to KE to PE to KE to PE … and then the process repeats…

You can Draw Graphs to Show Displacement, Velocity and Acceleration

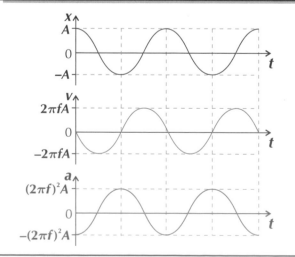

Displacement, **x**, varies as a cosine or sine wave with a maximum value, **A** (the amplitude).

Velocity, **v**, is the gradient of the displacement-time graph. It has a maximum value of $(2\pi f)A$ (where **f** is the frequency of the oscillation) and is a quarter of a cycle in front of the displacement.

Acceleration, **a**, is the gradient of the velocity-time graph. It has a maximum value of $(2\pi f)^2A$, and is in antiphase with the displacement.

Simple Harmonic Motion

The **Frequency** and **Period** don't depend on the **Amplitude**

1) From **maximum positive displacement** (e.g. maximum displacement to the right) to **maximum negative displacement** (e.g. maximum displacement to the left) and **back again** is called a **cycle** of oscillation.

2) The **frequency**, **f**, of the SHM is the number of cycles per second (measured in Hz).

3) The **period**, **T**, is the **time** taken for a complete cycle (in seconds).

> In SHM, the **frequency** and **period** are independent of the **amplitude** (i.e. constant for a given oscillation). So a pendulum clock will keep ticking in regular time intervals even if its swing becomes very small.

Learn the SHM Equations

I know it looks like there are loads of complicated equations to learn here, but don't panic — it's not that bad really. You'll be given these formulas in the exam, so just make sure you know what they mean and how to use them.

1) According to the definition of SHM, the **acceleration**, **a**, is directly proportional to the **displacement**, **x**. The **constant of proportionality** depends on the **frequency**, and the acceleration is always in the **opposite direction** from the displacement (so there's a minus sign in the equation).

$$a = -(2\pi f)^2 x$$

2) The **velocity** is **positive** if the object's moving **away** from the **midpoint**, and **negative** if it's moving **towards** the midpoint. It reaches a maximum, v_{max}, when the object is at the midpoint of its oscillation ($x = 0$).

Max velocity: $v_{max} = 2\pi f A$

A pendulum reaches maximum velocity at the bottom of each swing.

3) The **displacement** varies with time according to one of two equations, depending on **where** the object was when the timing was started. This determines whether the displacement-time graph is a cosine or sine wave.

> For someone starting a stopwatch with a pendulum at **maximum displacement**:
>
> $$x = A\cos(2\pi ft)$$

> For someone starting a stopwatch as the pendulum swings through **the midpoint**:
>
> $$x = A\sin(2\pi ft)$$

Practice Questions

Q1 Sketch a graph of how the velocity of an object oscillating with SHM varies with time.

Q2 What is the special relationship between the acceleration and the displacement in SHM?

Q3 Given the amplitude and the frequency, how would you work out the maximum acceleration?

Exam Questions

Q1 (a) Define *simple harmonic motion*. [2 marks]

(b) Explain why the motion of a ball bouncing off the ground is not SHM. [1 mark]

Q2 A pendulum is pulled a distance 0.05 m from its midpoint and released.
It oscillates with simple harmonic motion with a frequency of 1.5 Hz. Calculate:

(a) its maximum velocity [1 mark]

(b) its displacement 0.1 s after it is released [2 marks]

(c) the time it takes to fall to 0.01 m from the midpoint after it is released [2 marks]

"Simple" harmonic motion — hmmm, I'm not convinced...

The basic concept of SHM is simple enough (no pun intended). Make sure you can remember the shapes of all the graphs on page 14 and the equations from this page, then just get as much practice at using the equations as you can.

Free and Forced Vibrations

Resonance... hmm... tricky little beast. Remember the Millennium Bridge, that standard-bearer of British engineering? The wibbles and wobbles were caused by resonance. How was it sorted out? By damping, which is coming up too.

Free Vibrations — No Transfer of Energy To or From the Surroundings

1) If you stretch and release a mass on a spring, it oscillates at its **natural frequency**.

2) If **no energy's transferred** to or from the surroundings, it will **keep** oscillating with the **same amplitude forever**.

3) In practice this **never happens**, but a spring vibrating in air is called a **free vibration** anyway.

Forced Vibrations happen when there's an External Driving Force

1) A system can be **forced** to vibrate by a periodic **external force**.

2) The frequency of this force is called the **driving frequency**.

Resonance happens when Driving Frequency = Natural Frequency

When the **driving frequency** approaches the **natural frequency**, the system gains more and more energy from the driving force and so vibrates with a **rapidly increasing amplitude**. When this happens the system is **resonating**.

Mass oscillates with very large amplitude at the resonant frequency

Signal Generator — Sets driving frequency

Vibration Generator

How amplitude changes with driving frequency

amplitude

the natural frequency — driving frequency

Armies deliberately march 'out of step' when they cross a bridge. This reduces the risk of the bridge resonating and breaking apart.

Examples of resonance:

a) organ pipe

The column of air resonates, driven by the motion of air at the base.

b) swing

A swing resonates if it's driven by someone pushing it at its natural frequency.

c) glass smashing

A glass resonates when driven by a sound wave at the right frequency.

d) radio

A radio is tuned so the electric circuit resonates at the same frequency as the radio station you want to listen to.

Damping happens when Energy is Lost to the Surroundings

1) In practice, **any** oscillating system **loses energy** to its surroundings.

2) This is usually down to **frictional forces** like air resistance.

3) These are called **damping forces**.

4) Systems are often **deliberately damped** to **stop** them oscillating or to **minimise** the effect of **resonance**.

car body

suspension spring

shock absorber

axle

Shock absorbers in a car suspension provide a damping force by squashing oil through a hole when compressed.

Free and Forced Vibrations

Different Amounts of Damping have Different Effects

1) The **degree** of damping can vary from **light** damping (where the damping force is small) to **overdamping**.

2) Damping **reduces** the **amplitude** of the oscillation over time. The **heavier** the damping, the **quicker** the amplitude is reduced to zero.

3) **Critical damping** reduces the amplitude (i.e. stops the system oscillating) in the **shortest possible time**.

4) Car **suspension systems** and moving coil **meters** are critically damped so that they **don't oscillate** but return to equilibrium as quickly as possible.

5) Systems with **even heavier damping** are **overdamped**. They take **longer** to return to equilibrium than a critically damped system.

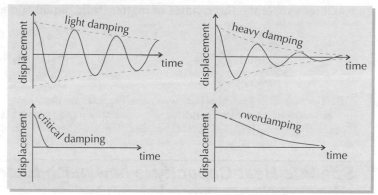

6) **Plastic deformation** of ductile materials **reduces** the **amplitude** of oscillations in the same way as damping. As the material changes shape, it **absorbs energy**, so the oscillation will become smaller.

Damping Affects Resonance too

1) **Lightly damped** systems have a **very sharp** resonance peak. Their amplitude only increases dramatically when the **driving frequency** is **very close** to the **natural frequency**.

2) **Heavily damped** systems have a **flatter response**. Their amplitude doesn't increase very much near the natural frequency and they aren't as **sensitive** to the driving frequency.

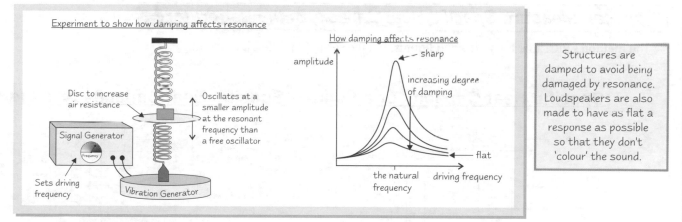

Structures are damped to avoid being damaged by resonance. Loudspeakers are also made to have as flat a response as possible so that they don't 'colour' the sound.

Practice Questions

Q1 What is a free vibration? What is a forced vibration?

Q2 Draw diagrams to show how a damped system oscillates with time when the system is lightly damped and when the system is critically damped.

Exam Questions

Q1 (a) What is resonance? [2 marks]
(b) Draw a diagram to show how the amplitude of a lightly damped system varies with driving frequency. [2 marks]
(c) On the same diagram, show how the amplitude of the system varies with driving frequency when it is heavily damped. [1 mark]

Q2 (a) What is critical damping? [1 mark]
(b) Describe a situation where critical damping is used. [1 mark]

A2 Physics — it can really put a damper on your social life...

Resonance can be really useful (radios, oboes, swings — yay) or very, <u>very</u> bad...

Solids, Liquids and Gases

You need energy to heat something up, and to change its state. Everything comes down to energy. Pretty much always.

The **Three States of Matter** are Defined by the **Arrangement of Particles**

You'll remember the **three states of matter** (**solid**, **liquid** and **gas**) from GCSE — but here's a quick recap just in case.

Solids

Particles vibrate about fixed positions in a regular lattice. They're held in position by strong forces of attraction.

Liquids

Particles are constantly moving around and are free to move past one another, but are attracted to each other.

Gases

Particles are free to move around with constant random motion. There are no forces of attraction between particles in an ideal gas.

Specific Heat Capacity is how much **Energy** it Takes to **Heat** Something

When you heat something — a solid, liquid or a gas — its particles get more **kinetic energy** and its **temperature** rises.

The **specific heat capacity** (**c**) of a substance is the amount of **energy** needed to **raise** the **temperature** of **1 kg** of the substance by **1 K** (or 1°C).

or put another way: energy change = mass × specific heat capacity × change in temperature

in symbols: $\Delta E = mc\Delta\theta$ ← ΔQ is sometimes used instead of ΔE for the change in thermal energy.

ΔE is the energy change in J, **m** is the mass in kg and $\Delta\theta$ is the temperature change in K or °C. Units of **c** are J kg⁻¹ K⁻¹ or J kg⁻¹ °C⁻¹.

You can **Measure** Specific Heat Capacity in the **Laboratory**

The **method**'s the same for **solids** and **liquids**, but the **set-up**'s a little bit different:

Specific Heat Capacity of a Solid

- Solid, e.g. metal cylinder
- Electric heater
- Digital thermometer
- Insulating material

Specific Heat Capacity of a Liquid

- Insulating lid
- Heating coil
- Digital thermometer
- Liquid
- Insulating material

Method for Both

1) **Heat** the substance with the heater. You need a **temperature rise** of about 10 K to get an **accurate** value of **c**. [NB The insulation **reduces** the heat loss, but it's far from perfect. If you're really keen, start **below** and finish **above** room temperature to **cancel out** gains and losses.]

2) With an ammeter and voltmeter attached to your **electric heater** you can work out the energy supplied. Here's the circuit:

    Calculate the energy (ΔE) using: $\Delta E = VI\Delta t$

    where *V* is the heater voltage, *I* is the current and Δt is the time in seconds (you should know this from AS).

3) Plug your data into: $\Delta E = mc\Delta\theta$ to calculate **c**.   The value you end up with for c will probably be too high by quite a long way. That's because some of the energy from the heater gets transferred to the air and the container.

Solids, Liquids and Gases

Use $\Delta E = mc\Delta\theta$ to Calculate Specific Heat Capacity

Example

You heat 0.25 kg of water from 12.1 °C to 22.9 °C with an electric immersion heater. The heater has a voltage of 11.2 V and a current of 5.3 A, and is switched on for 205 s.

Electrical energy supplied = $VI\Delta t$ = 11.2 × 5.3 × 205 = 12 170 J

Temperature rise = 22.9 – 12.1 = 10.8 °C = 10.8 K

So $c = \dfrac{12170}{0.25 \times 10.8} = 4510 \text{ Jkg}^{-1}\text{K}^{-1}$

The actual value for water is 4180 J kg^{-1} K^{-1}. This result's too big, because ΔE is bigger than it should be (like I said before).

Specific Latent Heat is Defined as the Latent Heat per kg

To **melt** a **solid**, you need to **break the bonds** that hold the particles in place. The **energy** needed for this is called the **latent heat of fusion**. Similarly, when you **boil or evaporate a liquid**, **energy is needed** to **pull the particles apart** completely. This is the **latent heat of vaporisation**.

The **larger** the **mass** of the substance, the **more energy** it takes to **change** its **state**. That's why the **specific latent heat** is defined per kg:

> The **specific latent heat (l)** of **fusion** or **vaporisation** is the quantity of **thermal energy** required to **change the state** of **1 kg** of a substance.

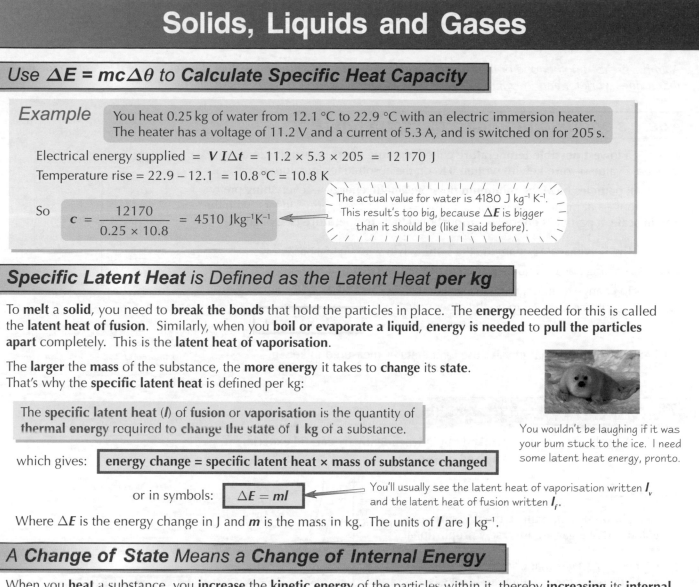

You wouldn't be laughing if it was your bum stuck to the ice. I need some latent heat energy, pronto.

which gives: **energy change = specific latent heat × mass of substance changed**

or in symbols: $\Delta E = ml$

You'll usually see the latent heat of vaporisation written l_v and the latent heat of fusion written l_f.

Where ΔE is the energy change in J and m is the mass in kg. The units of l are J kg^{-1}.

A Change of State Means a Change of Internal Energy

When you **heat** a substance, you **increase** the **kinetic energy** of the particles within it, thereby **increasing** its **internal energy** (page 24). When a substance **changes state**, its **internal energy** changes, but its **temperature doesn't**. This is because the **change of state** alters the **potential energy** of the particles — not their kinetic energy.

For example, each **molecule** of **water vapour (steam)** leaving a saucepan of boiling water has **more potential energy** than each molecule **in the pan**, even though the water in both states is at **100 °C**.

Practice Questions

Q1   Define specific heat capacity.

Q2   Describe how you would measure the specific heat capacity of olive oil.

Q3   Show that the thermal energy needed to heat 2 kg of water from 20 °C to 50 °C is ~250 kJ (c_{water} = 4180 Jkg^{-1}K^{-1}).

Q4   Explain why energy is needed to evaporate a liquid and define the specific latent heat of vaporisation.

Exam Questions

Q1   A 2 kg metal cylinder is heated uniformly from 4.5 °C to 12.7 °C in 3 minutes.
The electric heater used is rated at 12 V, 7.5 A.
Assuming that heat losses were negligible, calculate the specific heat capacity of the metal.   [3 marks]

Q2   A 3 kW electric kettle contains 0.5 kg of water already at its boiling point.

(a) Explain how two molecules of the water can have different energies.   [3 marks]

(b) Neglecting heat losses, how long will it take to boil dry? (l_v (water) = 2.26 × 10^6 J kg^{-1})   [3 marks]

My specific eat capacity — 24 pies...

*This stuff's a bit dull, but hey... make sure you're comfortable using those equations. Interesting(ish) fact for the day — it's the **huge** difference in specific heat capacity between the land and the sea that causes the monsoon in Asia. So there.*

Ideal Gases

*Aaahh... great... another one of those 'our equation doesn't work properly with **real gases**, so we'll invent an **ideal** gas that it **does work** for and they'll think we're dead clever' situations. Hmm. Physicists, eh...*

There's an **Absolute Scale** of **Temperature**

There is a **lowest possible temperature** called **absolute zero***. Absolute zero is given a value of **zero kelvin**, written **0 K**, on the absolute temperature scale.

At **0 K** all particles have the **minimum** possible **kinetic energy** — everything pretty much stops — at higher temperatures, particles have more energy. In fact, with the **Kelvin scale**, a particle's **energy** is **proportional** to its **temperature** (see page 25).

1) The Kelvin scale is named after Lord Kelvin who first suggested it.

2) A change of **1 K** equals a change of **1 °C**.

3) To change from degrees Celsius into kelvin you **add 273.15** (or subtract 273.15 to go the other way).

$$K = C + 273.15$$

All equations in **thermal physics** use temperatures measured in kelvin.

Equivalent temperatures
373 K — 100 °C
273 K — 0 °C
0 K — −273 °C

*It's true. −273.15 °C is the lowest temperature theoretically possible. Weird, huh. You'd kinda think there wouldn't be a minimum, but there is.

There are **Three Gas Laws**

The three gas laws were each worked out **independently** by **careful experiment**. Each of the gas laws applies to a **fixed mass** of gas.

Boyle's Law

At a **constant temperature** the **pressure p** and **volume V** of a gas are **inversely proportional**.

A (theoretical) gas that obeys Boyle's law at all temperatures is called an **ideal gas**.

The higher the temperature of the gas, the further the curve is from the origin.

$$pV = \text{constant}$$

Charles' Law

At constant **pressure**, the **volume V** of a gas is **directly proportional** to its **absolute temperature T**.

Ideal gases obey this law and the pressure law as well.

For any ideal gas, the line meets the temperature axis at −273.15 °C — that is, absolute zero.

$$V/T = \text{constant}$$

'Ello, 'ello...

The Pressure Law

At constant **volume**, the **pressure p** of a gas is **directly proportional** to its **absolute temperature T**.

If you'd plotted these graphs in kelvin, they'd both have gone through the origin.

$$p/T = \text{constant}$$

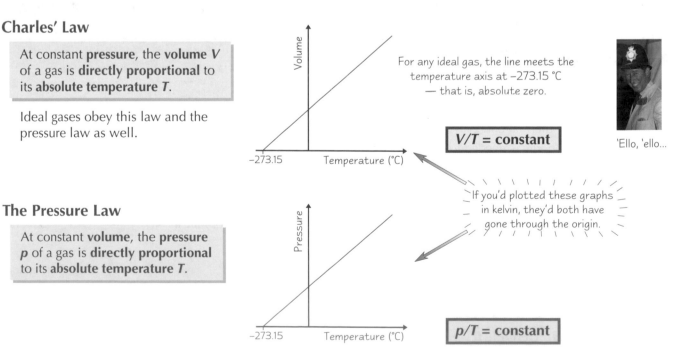

Ideal Gases

If you **Combine** All Three you get the **Ideal Gas Equation**

Combining all three gas laws gives the equation: $p\dfrac{V}{T} = $ **constant**

1) The constant in the equation depends on the amount of gas used. ⟵ (Pretty obvious... if you have more gas it takes up more space.)
   The amount of **gas** can be **measured** in **moles**, *n*.

2) The constant then becomes *nR*, where *R* is called the **molar gas constant**.
   Its value is 8.31 J mol⁻¹ K⁻¹.

3) Plugging this into the equation gives:
   $$p\frac{V}{T} = nR \quad \text{or rearranging,} \quad pV = nRT - \text{the ideal gas equation}$$

This equation works well (i.e., real gases approximate an ideal gas) for gases at **low pressure** and fairly **high temperatures**.

Boltzmann's Constant k is like a **Gas Constant** for **One Particle** of **Gas**

One mole of any **gas** contains the same number of particles.
This number is called **Avogadro's constant** and has the symbol N_A. The value of N_A is **6.02 × 10²³ particles per mole**.

1) The **number of particles** in a **mass of gas** is given by the **number of moles**, *n*, multiplied by **Avogadro's constant**.
   So the number of particles, $N = nN_A$.

2) **Boltzmann's constant**, *k*, is equivalent to R/N_A — you can think of Boltzmann's constant as the **gas constant** for **one particle of gas**, while *R* is the gas constant for **one mole of gas**.

3) The value of Boltzmann's constant is **1.38 × 10⁻²³ JK⁻¹**.

4) If you combine $N = nN_A$ and $k = R/N_A$ you'll see that $Nk = nR$
   — which can be substituted into the ideal gas equation: ⟶
   $$pV = NkT - \text{the equation of state}$$

   The equation $pV = NkT$ is called the equation of state of an ideal gas.

Practice Questions

Q1 State Boyle's law, Charles' law and the pressure law.

Q2 What is the ideal gas equation?

Q3 The pressure of a gas is 100 000 Pa and its temperature is 27 °C. The gas is heated — its volume stays fixed but the pressure rises to 150 000 Pa. Show that its new temperature is 177 °C.

Q4 What is the equation of state of an ideal gas?

Exam Questions

Q1 The mass of one mole of nitrogen gas is 0.028 kg. R = 8.31 J mol⁻¹ K⁻¹.

   (a) A flask contains 0.014 kg of nitrogen gas.

      i) How many moles of nitrogen gas are in the flask? [1 mark]

      ii) How many nitrogen molecules are in the flask? [1 mark]

   (b) The flask has a volume of 0.01 m³ and is at a temperature of 27 °C. What is the pressure inside it? [2 marks]

   (c) What would happen to the pressure if the number of molecules of nitrogen in the flask was halved? [1 mark]

Q2 A large helium balloon has a volume of 10 m³ at ground level.
   The temperature of the gas in the balloon is 293 K and the pressure is 1 × 10⁵ Pa.
   The balloon is released and rises to a height where its volume becomes 25 m³ and its temperature is 260 K.
   Calculate the pressure inside the balloon at its new height. [3 marks]

Ideal revision equation — marks = (pages read × questions answered)²...

*All this might sound a bit theoretical, but most gases you'll meet in the everyday world come fairly close to being 'ideal'.
They only stop obeying these laws when the pressure's too high or they're getting close to their boiling point.*

The Pressure of an Ideal Gas

Kinetic theory tries to explain the gas laws. It basically models a gas as a series of hard balls that obey Newton's laws.

You Can Use Newton's Laws to Derive the Pressure of an Ideal Gas

Imagine a cubic box containing *N* particles of an ideal gas, each with a mass *m*.

See pages 6-7 for a recap of Newton's laws.

1) The particles of the gas are **free to move** around with **constant random motion**. There are **no forces of attraction** between the particles, so according to **Newton's 1st law**, they continue to move with **constant velocity** until they collide with another particle or the box itself.

2) When a particle **collides** with a **wall** of the box, it exerts a **force** on the wall, and the wall exerts an **equal and opposite force** on the particle. This is **Newton's 3rd law** in action.

3) The **size of the force** exerted by the particle on the wall can be **calculated** using **Newton's 2nd law**, which says the **force is proportional to the rate of change of momentum**.

4) For example, if particle **Q** is travelling directly towards wall **A** with velocity **u**, its momentum is **mu**. When it **hits** the wall, the force of the **impact** causes it to rebound in the **opposite direction**, at the same speed. Its **momentum** is now **–mu**, which means the **change in momentum** is 2**mu**.

5) So, the **force** a particle exerts is **proportional** to its **mass** and its **velocity**. The **mass** of a single **gas particle** is **tiny** (for example, an atom of helium gas is only 6.6×10^{-27} kg), so each particle can only exert a **minuscule force**.

6) But, there **isn't** just **one particle** in the box — there's probably **millions of billions** of them. The **combined force** from so many tiny particles is **much bigger** than the contribution from any individual particle.

Imagine putting a single grain of sugar into a lunchbox and shaking it around — the box might as well be empty. Now put a couple of spoonfuls of sugar in, and shake that around — this time you'll hear the sugar thumping against the walls of the box as it collides. You don't notice the effect of the individual grains, only the combined action of loads of them.

7) Because there are so many particles in the box, a **significant number** will be **colliding** with each wall of the box at **any given moment**. And because the particles' motion is **random**, the **collisions** will be **spread** all over the surface of each wall. The result is a **steady**, **even force** on all the walls of the box — this is **pressure**.

Pressure is Proportional to the Number of Particles, their Mass and Speed

So, the pressure in a gas is a result of all the collisions between particles and the walls of the container. How much pressure is exerted by the gas depends on four things:

1) The **volume** of the container — increasing the volume of the container decreases the **frequency of collisions** because the particles have **further to travel** in between collisions. This decreases the pressure.

2) The **number of particles** — increasing the number of particles increases the **frequency of collisions** between the particles and the container, so increases the **total force** exerted by all the collisions.

3) The **mass of the particles** — according to Newton's 2nd law, **force is proportional to mass**, so **heavier** particles will exert a **greater force**.

4) The **speed of the particles** — the **faster** the particles are going when they collide, the **greater** the **change in momentum** and force exerted.

Or, in symbols: $pV \propto Nm\overline{c^2}$

($\overline{c^2}$ is the mean square speed — it represents the square of the speed of a <u>typical particle</u>.)

The Pressure of an Ideal Gas

Lots of **Simplifying Assumptions** are Used in **Kinetic Theory**

In **kinetic theory**, physicists picture gas particles moving at **high speed** in **random directions**.
To get relations like the one on the previous page, some **simplifying assumptions** are needed:

1) The gas contains a **large number of particles**.
2) The particles **move rapidly** and **randomly**.
3) The motion of the particles follows **Newton's laws**.
4) **Collisions** between particles themselves or between particles and the walls of the container are **perfectly elastic**.
5) There are **no attractive forces** between particles.
6) Any **forces** that act during collisions are **instantaneous**.
7) Particles have a **negligible volume** compared with the volume of the container.

Don't make an ass of yourself — learn the assumptions.

A **gas obeying** these **assumptions** is called an **ideal** gas. Real gases behave like ideal gases as long as the **pressure isn't too big** and the **temperature** is **reasonably high** (compared with their boiling points).

Brownian Motion Supports Kinetic Theory

In 1827, the botanist **Robert Brown** noticed that pollen grains in water constantly moved with a zigzag, **random motion**.

Brownian Motion Experiment

You can **observe** Brownian motion in the lab.

Put some **smoke** in a **brightly illuminated** glass jar and observe the particles using a **microscope**.

The smoke particles appear as **bright specks** moving **haphazardly** from side to side, and up and down.

Brown couldn't explain this, but nearly 80 years later Einstein showed that this provided evidence for the existence of atoms or **molecules** in the air. The **randomly moving** air particles were hitting the smoke particles unevenly, causing this motion.

microscope →

glass cell
containing
smoke

lamp   glass
rod to
focus light

Practice Questions

Q1 Describe the connection between collisions and pressure in an ideal gas.
Q2 What are the seven assumptions made about ideal gas behaviour?
Q3 What did Robert Brown observe?
Q4 Why do smoke particles show Brownian motion?

Exam Question

Q1 Brownian motion provides evidence for the continual random motion of particles in a gas.

(a) Describe an experiment you could use to demonstrate Brownian motion. [2 marks]

(b) Explain how Brownian motion supports the theory of the random movement of particles. [2 marks]

(c) Outline how the random movement of particles accounts for pressure in a gas. [1 mark]

Brownian motion — Girl Guide in a tumble-drier...

Pardon me if I'm wrong, but I thought science was all about making predictions and testing them with good old experiments — not having an idea and then creating a load of assumptions to make it work. Hmmm — physicists, eh...

Internal Energy and Temperature

*The energy of a particle depends on its temperature on the **thermodynamic scale** (that's Kelvin to you and me).*

If **A** and **B** are in **Thermal Equilibrium** with **C**, **A** is in **Equilibrium** with **B**

If **body A** and **body B** are both in **thermal equilibrium** with **body C**, then **body A** and **body B** must be in thermal equilibrium with **each other**.

This is linked with the idea of **temperature**.

1) Suppose A, B and C are three identical metal blocks. A has been in a **warm oven**, B has come from a **refrigerator** and C is at **room temperature**.

2) **Thermal energy** flows from A to C and C to B until they all reach **thermal equilibrium** and the net flow of energy stops. This happens when the three blocks are at the **same temperature**.

Thermal energy is **always** transferred from regions of **higher temperature** to regions of **lower temperature**.

The **Speed Distribution** of **Gas Particles** Depends on **Temperature**

The **particles** in a **gas don't** all **travel** at the **same speed**. Some particles will be moving fast but others much more slowly. Most will travel around the average speed. The shape of the **speed distribution** depends on the **temperature** of the gas.

As the temperature of the gas increases:
1) the **average** particle speed increases.
2) the **maximum** particle speed increases.
3) the distribution curve becomes more **spread out**.

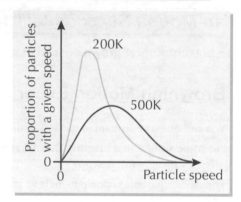

Energy Changes Happen Between Particles

The particles of a gas **collide** with each other **all the time**. Some of these collisions will be '**head-on**' (particles moving in **opposite directions**) while others will be '**shunts from behind**' (particles moving in the **same direction**).

1) As a result of the collisions, **energy** will be **transferred** between particles.
2) Some particles will **gain speed** in a collision and others will **slow down**.
3) **Between collisions**, the particles will travel at **constant speed**.
4) Although the energy of an individual particle changes at each collision, the collisions **don't** alter the **total energy** of the **system**.
5) So, the **average** speed of the particles will stay the same provided the **temperature** of the gas **stays the same**.

Internal Energy is the **Sum** of **Kinetic** and **Potential Energy**

All things (solids, liquids, gases) have **energy** contained within them. The amount of **energy** contained in a system is called its **internal energy** — it's found by **summing** the **kinetic** and **potential energy** of all the **particles** within it.

Internal energy is the **sum** of the **kinetic** and **potential energy** of the **particles** within a system.

For example, the **internal energy** of an **ideal gas** is due to the **kinetic energy** of the **particles** within it. But, how do you **sum** the **individual energies** when the particles all move at **different speeds**, so have **different kinetic energies**? The answer is to find the **average kinetic energy** of a particle (page 25), then **multiply** by the number of particles.

Internal Energy and Temperature

Average Kinetic Energy is Proportional to Absolute Temperature

If you've been paying attention to this section, you'll know that $pV = NkT$ (this is the **equation of state** from page 21) and that pV is **proportional** to $Nm\overline{c^2}$ (page 22). You can **combine** these to find the **kinetic energy** of gas particles.

1) The **equation of state**: $pV = NkT$

2) The **pressure** of an **ideal gas** given by kinetic theory: $pV \propto Nm\overline{c^2}$

$\overline{c^2}$ represents the square of the speed of a typical particle.

3) **Equating** these two gives: $Nm\overline{c^2} \propto NkT$

4) And you can **cancel** N to give: $m\overline{c^2} \propto kT$

N is the number of particles in the gas.

m is the mass of one particle in the gas.

5) $\frac{1}{2}m\overline{c^2}$ is the **average kinetic energy** of an **individual particle**. (Remember $\overline{c^2}$ is a measure of speed squared, so this is just like the equation for kinetic energy, $KE = \frac{1}{2}mv^2$, that you'll know already.)

6) This means that kT is **proportional** to **average kinetic energy**:

$$E = \frac{3}{2}kT$$

T is the absolute temperature.

The kinetic energy of gas particles is always an average value because the particles are all travelling at different speeds

k is Boltzmann's constant 1.38 × 10⁻²³ JK⁻¹

The **internal energy** of an ideal gas is the **product** of the **average kinetic energy** of its particles and the **number of particles** within it. **Average kinetic energy** is directly proportional to the **absolute temperature** (see above), so **internal energy** must also be **dependent** on **temperature** — a **rise** in the **absolute temperature** will cause an **increase** in the kinetic energy of each particle, meaning a rise in **internal energy**.

Practice Questions

Q1   Describe the changes in the distribution of gas particle speeds as the temperature of a gas increases.

Q2   What is internal energy?

Q3   What would cause a rise in internal energy?

Q4   What happens to the average kinetic energy of a particle if the temperature of a gas doubles?

Exam Questions

Q1   A flask contains one mole of nitrogen molecules at 300 K.
(a) How many molecules of nitrogen are in the flask?   [1 mark]
(b) Calculate the average kinetic energy of a nitrogen molecule in the flask.   [2 marks]
(c) Explain why all the nitrogen molecules in the flask will not have the same kinetic energy.   [1 mark]

Q2   A container of neon gas is cooled until its absolute temperature halves.
Describe and explain any change in the following quantities caused by the cooling:
(i)   the average kinetic energy of a molecule of neon gas
(ii) the internal energy of the gas
(iv) the mass of a molecule of neon gas
(iii) the pressure within the container   [4 marks]

Positivise your internal energy, man...

Phew... there's a lot to take in on these pages. Go back over it, step by step, and make sure you understand it all: the speed distribution of particles, internal energy, average kinetic energy, your A,B,Cs...

Electric Fields

*Electric fields can be attractive or repulsive, so they're different from gravitational ones. It's all to do with **charge**.*

There is an **Electric Field** around a **Charged Object**

Any object with **charge** has an **electric field** around it — the region where it can attract or repel other charges.

1) Electric charge, **Q**, is measured in **coulombs** (C) and can be either positive or negative.
2) **Oppositely** charged particles **attract** each other. **Like** charges **repel**.
3) If a **charged object** is placed in an electric field, then it will experience a **force**.

You can **Calculate Forces** using **Coulomb's Law**

You'll need **Coulomb's law** to work out **F** — the force of attraction or repulsion between two point charges...

COULOMB'S LAW:

$$F = \frac{kQ_1Q_2}{r^2} \quad \text{where} \quad k = \frac{1}{4\pi\varepsilon}$$

If the charges are **opposite** then the force is **attractive**. F will be **negative**.

If Q_1 and Q_2 are **like** charges then the force is **repulsive**, and F will be **positive**.

ε ("epsilon") = permittivity of material between charges
Q_1 and Q_2 are the charges
r is the distance between Q_1 and Q_2

1) The force on Q_1 is always **equal** and **opposite** to the force on Q_2.
2) It's an **inverse square law**. Again. The further apart the charges are, the weaker the force between them.
3) The size of the force **F** also depends on the **permittivity**, ε, of the material between the two charges. For free space, the permittivity is $\varepsilon_0 = 8.85 \times 10^{-12} \, C^2N^{-1}m^{-2}$.

Electric Field Strength is Force per Unit Charge

Electric field strength, **E**, is defined as the **force per unit positive charge** — the force that a charge of +1 C would experience if it was placed in the electric field.

$$E = \frac{F}{q}$$

F is the force on a 'test' charge **q**.

1) **E** is a **vector** pointing in the **direction** that a **positive charge** would **move**.
2) The units of **E** are **newtons per coulomb** (NC^{-1}).
3) Field strength depends on **where you are** in the field.
4) A **point charge** — or any body which behaves as if all its charge is concentrated at the centre — has a **radial** field.

In a **Radial Field**, E is Inversely Proportional to r²

1) **E** is the force per unit charge that a small, positive 'test' charge, **q**, would feel at different points in the field. In a **radial field**, **E** depends on the distance **r** from the point charge **Q**...

$$E = \frac{kQ}{r^2} \quad \left(k = \frac{1}{4\pi\varepsilon}\right)$$

For a **positive Q**, the small positive 'test' charge **q** would be **repelled**, so the field lines point **away** from **Q**.

For a **negative Q**, the small positive charge **q** would be **attracted**, so the field lines point **towards Q**.

2) It's another **inverse square law** — $E \propto \frac{1}{r^2}$

3) Field strength **decreases** as you go **further away** from **Q** — on a diagram, the **field lines** get **further apart**.

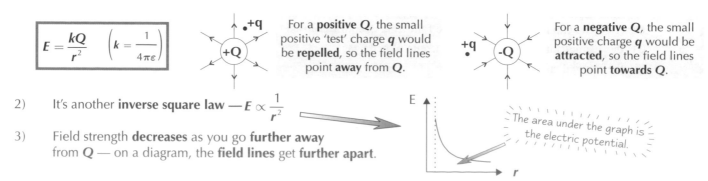

The area under the graph is the electric potential.

Electric Fields

Field Strength is the Same Everywhere in a Uniform Field

A **uniform field** can be produced by connecting two **parallel plates** to the opposite poles of a battery.

1) Field strength **E** is the **same** at **all points** between the two plates and is...

$$E = \frac{V}{d}$$

V is the **potential difference** between the plates
d is the distance between them

The **lines of force** are **parallel** to each other.

Areas with the **same potential** are **parallel** to the **plates**, and **perpendicular** to the **field lines**.

2) **E** can be measured in volts per metre (Vm⁻¹).

Charged Particles Move Through Uniform Electric Fields Like Projectiles

You'll probably remember from AS that **projectiles** move through a **uniform gravitational field** along a curved path called a **parabola**. **Charged particles** do a similar thing when they move through **uniform electric fields**.

1) A charged particle will experience a **constant force parallel** to the **electric field lines**.

2) If the particle is **positively charged** then the force is in the **same direction** as the field lines.
    If it's **negatively charged** (e.g. an **electron**), the force is in the **opposite direction** to the field lines.

3) The particle will **accelerate at a constant rate** in the direction of this force — that's just **Newton's second law**.

4) If the particle's **velocity** has a **component** at **right angles** to the field lines, the particle will keep moving in this direction with a **uniform velocity**. That's **Newton's first law**.

5) The combined effect of constant acceleration in one direction and constant velocity at right angles is a **parabola**.

There are Similarities between Gravitational and Electric Fields...

1)	Gravitational field strength, **g**, is **force** per **unit mass**.	Electric field strength, **E**, is **force** per **unit positive charge**.
2)	Newton's law of gravitation for the **force** between two point masses is an **inverse square law**. $F \propto \frac{1}{r^2}$	Coulomb's law for the electric **force** between two point charges is also an **inverse square law**. $F \propto \frac{1}{r^2}$
3)	A point mass creates a **radial gravitational field**.	A point charge creates a **radial electric field**.

... and some Differences too

1) Gravitational forces are always **attractive**. Electric forces can be either **attractive** or **repulsive**.

2) Objects can be **shielded** from **electric** fields, but not from gravitational fields.

3) The **medium** between the charges or masses affects the **size** of **electric forces**, but not gravitational forces.

Practice Questions

Q1   Draw the electric field lines due to a positive charge, and due to a negative charge.
Q2   Write down Coulomb's law.

Exam Questions

Q1   The diagram shows two electric charges with equal but opposite charge, Q.
      Draw electric field lines to show the electric field in the area surrounding the charges.   ●+Q   ●-Q   [3 marks]

Q2   Find the electric field strength at a distance of 1.75×10^{-10} m from a 1.6×10^{-19} C point charge.   [2 marks]

Q3 (a) Two parallel plates are separated by an air gap of 4.5 mm. The plates are connected to a 1500 V dc supply.
       What is the electric field strength between the plates? Give a suitable unit and state the direction of the field. [3 marks]

   (b) The plates are now pulled further apart so that the distance between them is doubled.
       The electric field strength remains the same. What is the new voltage between the plates?   [2 marks]

Electric fields — one way to roast beef...

At least you get a choice here — uniform or radial, positive or negative, attractive or repulsive, chocolate or strawberry...

Magnetic Fields

Magnetic fields — making pretty patterns with iron filings before spending an age trying to pick them off the magnet.

A **Magnetic Field** is a **Region** Where a **Force** is Exerted on **Magnetic Materials**

1) Magnetic fields can be represented by **field lines**.
2) Field lines go from **north to south**.
3) The **closer** together the lines, the **stronger** the field.
4) At a **neutral point**, the magnetic fields **cancel out**.

A neutral point

There is a **Magnetic Field** Around a **Wire** Carrying **Electric Current**

1) When **current flows** in a wire (or any other long straight conductor), there's a **magnetic field** around the wire.

2) The **field lines** form **concentric circles** centred on the wire — the **closer** together the circles are, the **stronger** the field.

3) The **direction** of a magnetic **field** around a current-carrying wire can be worked out with the **right-hand rule**. ⇒

4) If you wrap the wire around to make a **single coil** or a **solenoid**, the shape of the **field changes** as the lines interact.

RIGHT-HAND RULE

1) Stick your <u>right thumb</u> up, like you're hitching a lift.
2) If your <u>thumb</u> points in the direction of the <u>current</u>...
3) ...your curled <u>fingers</u> point in the direction of the <u>field</u>.

coil

field lines

solenoid

field lines

The magnetic field around a solenoid is the same shape as the one around a bar magnet.

A **Wire** Carrying a **Current** in a **Magnetic Field** will **Experience** a **Force**

1) If you put a **current-carrying wire** into an **external** magnetic field (e.g. between two magnets), the field around the wire and the field from the magnets **interact**. The field lines from the magnet **contract** to form a **'stretched catapult'** effect where the flux lines are closer together. ⇒

2) This causes a **force** on the wire.

3) If the current is **parallel** to the flux lines, **no force** acts.

4) The **direction** of the force is always **perpendicular** to both the **current** direction and the **magnetic field** — it's given by **Fleming's left-hand rule**...

↑ Resulting Force

N   S

→   Normal magnetic field of wire
→   Normal magnetic field of magnets
→   Deviated magnetic field of magnets

The **Direction** of the **Force** is Given by **Fleming's Left-Hand Rule**

You can work out the direction of the **force** on a **current-carrying wire** using **Fleming's left-hand rule** — just remember to use your **left hand**...

Fleming's Left-Hand Rule

The First finger points in the direction of the uniform magnetic Field, the seCond finger points in the direction of the conventional Current. Then your thuMb points in the direction of the force (in which Motion takes place).

Field lines
Current in wire
Force

Motion (force)

Magnetic field N to S

Current (+ to -)

Magnetic Fields

The Size of the Force can be Calculated using F = BIl...

1) The size of the **force**, **F**, on a current-carrying wire at right-angles to a magnetic field is proportional to the **current**, **I**, the **length of wire** in the field, **I**, and the **strength of the magnetic field**, **B**. This gives the equation:

$$F = BIl$$

2) In this equation, the **magnetic field strength**, **B**, is defined as:

> The **force** on **one metre** of wire carrying a **current** of **one amp** at **right angles** to the **magnetic field**.

3) **Magnetic field strength** is also called **flux density** and it's measured in **teslas**, **T**.

$$1 \text{ tesla} = \frac{Wb}{m^2}$$

It helps to think of <u>flux density</u> as the number of <u>flux lines</u> (measured in webers (Wb), see p 30) <u>per unit area</u>.

4) Magnetic field strength is a **vector** quantity with both a **direction** and **magnitude**.

The Force is Greatest when the Wire and Field are Perpendicular...

1) The **force** on a current-carrying wire in a magnetic field is caused by the **component** of field strength which is **perpendicular** to the wire — **B sin θ**.

2) So, for a wire at an **angle θ** to the field, the **force** acting on the wire is given by:

Field   B   Current
B sin θ   θ

$$F = BIl \sin \theta$$

Examples:

i) θ — If θ = 90°, F = BIl

ii) θ — If θ = 30°, F = BIl × 0.5

iii) — If θ = 0°, F = 0

→ current
→ magnetic field

Practice Questions

Q1 Describe why a current-carrying wire at right angles to an external magnetic field will experience a force.

Q2 Write down the equation you would use to find the force on a current-carrying wire that is at an angle of 30° to an external uniform field.

Q3 Sketch the magnetic fields around a long straight current-carrying wire and a solenoid. Show the direction of the current and magnetic field on each diagram.

Q4 A copper bar can roll freely on two copper supports, as shown in the diagram. When current is applied in the direction shown, which way will the bar roll?

Horseshoe magnet
N
S
Copper bar

Exam Question

Q1 A 4 cm length of wire carrying a current of 3 A runs perpendicular to a magnetic field of strength 2×10^{-5} T.

  (a) Calculate the magnitude of the force on the wire.   [2 marks]

  (b) If the wire is rotated so that it is at 30° to the direction of the field, what would the size of the force be?   [2 marks]

I revised the right hand rule by the A69 and ended up in Newcastle...

Fleming's left-hand rule is the key to this section — so make sure you know how to use it and understand what it all means. Remember that the direction of the magnetic field is from N to S, and that the current is from +ve to –ve — this is as important as using the correct hand. You need to get those right or it'll all go to pot...

Charged Particles in Magnetic Fields

Magnetic fields are used a lot when dealing with particle beams.

Forces Act on Charged Particles in Magnetic Fields

Electric current in a wire is caused by the **flow** of negatively **charged** electrons. These charged particles are affected by **magnetic fields** — so a current-carrying wire experiences a **force** in a magnetic field (see pages 28–29).

1) The equation for the **force** exerted on a **current-carrying wire** in a **magnetic field** perpendicular to the current is:

    Equation 1: $\boxed{F = BIl}$

2) To see how this relates to **charged particles** moving through a wire, you need to know that electric **current**, I, is the flow of **charge**, q, per unit **time**, t:

    $$I = \frac{q}{t}$$

3) A charged particle which moves a **distance** l in **time** t has a **velocity**, v:

    $$v = \frac{l}{t} \Rightarrow t = \frac{l}{v}$$

In many exam questions, q is the size of the charge on the electron, which is 1.6×10^{-19} coulombs.

4) So, putting the two equations **together** gives the **current** in terms of the **charge** flowing through the **wire**:

    Equation 2: $\boxed{I = \frac{qv}{l}}$

5) Putting **equation 2** back into **equation 1** gives the **electromagnetic force** on the wire as:

    $$\boxed{F = Bqv}$$

6) You can use this equation to find the **force** acting on a **single charged particle** moving through a magnetic field.

Example

What is the force acting on an electron travelling at 2×10^4 ms^{-1} through a uniform magnetic field of strength 2 T?
(The magnitude of the charge on an electron is 1.6×10^{-19} C.)

$$F = Bqv$$
so, $\quad F = 2 \times 1.6 \times 10^{-19} \times 2 \times 10^4$
so, $\quad F = 6.4 \times 10^{-15}$ N

Charged Particles in a Magnetic Field are Deflected in a Circular Path

1) By **Fleming's left-hand rule** the force on a **moving charge** in a magnetic field is always **perpendicular** to its **direction of travel**.

2) Mathematically, that is the condition for **circular** motion.

3) This effect is used in **particle accelerators** such as **cyclotrons** and **synchrotrons**, which use **magnetic fields** to accelerate particles to very **high energies** along circular paths.

4) The **radius of curvature** of the **path** of a charged particle moving through a magnetic field gives you information about the particle's **charge** and **mass** — this means you can **identify different particles** by studying how they're **deflected** (see next page).

Centripetal Force Tells Us About a Particle's Path

The centripetal force and the electromagnetic force are equivalent for a charged particle travelling along a circular path.

Centripetal force   Electromagnetic force

1) For uniform circular motion **Newton's second law** gives: $\boxed{F = \frac{mv^2}{r}}$

2) So, for a **charged particle** following a **circular** path in a **magnetic field** (where $F = Bqv$): $\boxed{Bqv = \frac{mv^2}{r}}$

3) Rearranging gives: $\boxed{r = \frac{mv}{Bq}}$

Where: m is the mass of the particle, v is its speed and r is the radius of the circular path.

Charged Particles in Magnetic Fields

Scientists use Mass Spectrometers to Analyse Samples

1) **Mass spectrometers** are used to **analyse samples** to find out what **chemicals** are present within them and the **relative proportions** of each one.

2) First, the sample is **vaporised** (i.e. turned to gas) and **ionised** before passing along the **spectrometer tube**.

3) The ions travel through **electric** and **magnetic fields** to a **detector**, which is connected to a **computer**.

4) The **identity** of the **ions** reaching the **detector** can be determined from their **mass to charge ratio**.

A Mass Spectrometer

The Electric Field Accelerates the Ions...

1) The **ions** are **charged**, so they experience a **force** as they travel through the **electric field**.

2) This force **accelerates** the ions along the **evacuated spectrometer tube** towards the magnetic field.

3) The **velocity** of the ions depends on the **electric field strength** — **increasing** the **field strength** increases the **force** on the ions, so **increases** their **acceleration** and final **velocity**.

... And the Magnetic Field Deflects the Ions in a Circular Path

1) The **magnetic field** deflects the ions in a **circular path** (see the previous page).

2) The **radius** of the path of each **ion** depends on its **mass to charge ratio**, its **velocity** and the strength of the **magnetic field** — see the equation at the bottom of the previous page.

3) The **velocity** of the ions and the **magnetic field strength** can be **controlled** by the user.

4) Only the **ions** moving in an arc of a particular **radius** can pass through the slit into the **detector**.

5) This means that only ions with a particular **mass to charge ratio** reach the **detector** at any one time.

6) The detector is connected to a **computer**, which **identifies the ions** from their **mass to charge ratio** and the spectrometer settings, and records the **amount** of each ion.

The field had deflected the lions onto a circular path.

Practice Questions

Q1 Derive the formula for the force on a charged particle in a magnetic field, **F = Bqv**, from **F = BIl**.

Q2 Give two examples of how magnetic fields can be used.

Q3 Outline the role of the electric and magnetic fields in a mass spectrometer.

Exam Questions

Q1 (a) What is the force on an electron travelling at a velocity of 5×10^6 ms^{-1} through a perpendicular magnetic field of 0.77 T? [The charge on an electron is -1.6×10^{-19} C.] [2 marks]

(b) Explain why it follows a circular path while in the field. [1 mark]

Q2 What is the radius of the circular path of an electron with a velocity of 2.3×10^7 ms^{-1} moving perpendicular to a magnetic field of 0.6 mT?
[The mass of an electron is 9.11×10^{-31} kg and its charge is -1.6×10^{-19} C.] [3 marks]

Q3 A sample of sodium chloride is analysed using a mass spectrometer. The magnetic field is initially set to 0.20 T and ions of the isotope Cl-35 (mass 35 u) reach the detector. What magnetic field strength would you need for Cl-37 ions (mass 37 u) to reach the detector? Assume that the detector remains in the same place, the electric field remains constant and that both types of ion have the same size charge as an electron. [3 marks]

Hold on to your hats folks — this is starting to get tricky...

Basically, the main thing you need to know here is that both electric and magnetic fields will exert a force on a charged particle. There's even a handy equation to work out the force on a charged particle moving through a magnetic field — it might not impress your friends, but it will impress the examiner, so learn it.

Electromagnetic Induction

Producing electricity by waggling a wire about in a magnetic field sounds like monkey magic — but it's real physics...

Think of the **Magnetic Flux** as the Total **Number** of **Field Lines**...

1) Magnetic field strength, or **magnetic flux density**, **B**, is a measure of the **strength** of a magnetic field **per unit area**.

2) It depends on the concentration of **field lines** or **magnetic flux** passing through that area.

3) The total **magnetic flux**, ϕ, passing through an **area**, **A**, perpendicular to a **magnetic field**, **B**, is defined as: $\longrightarrow$ $\boxed{\phi = BA}$

The unit of ϕ ('phi') is the weber — see below for a definition.

If the magnetic flux is **not perpendicular** to **B**, you can find the **magnetic flux** using this equation:

$$\boxed{\phi = BA \cos \theta}$$

where θ is the **angle** between the **field** and the **normal** to the plane of the coil.

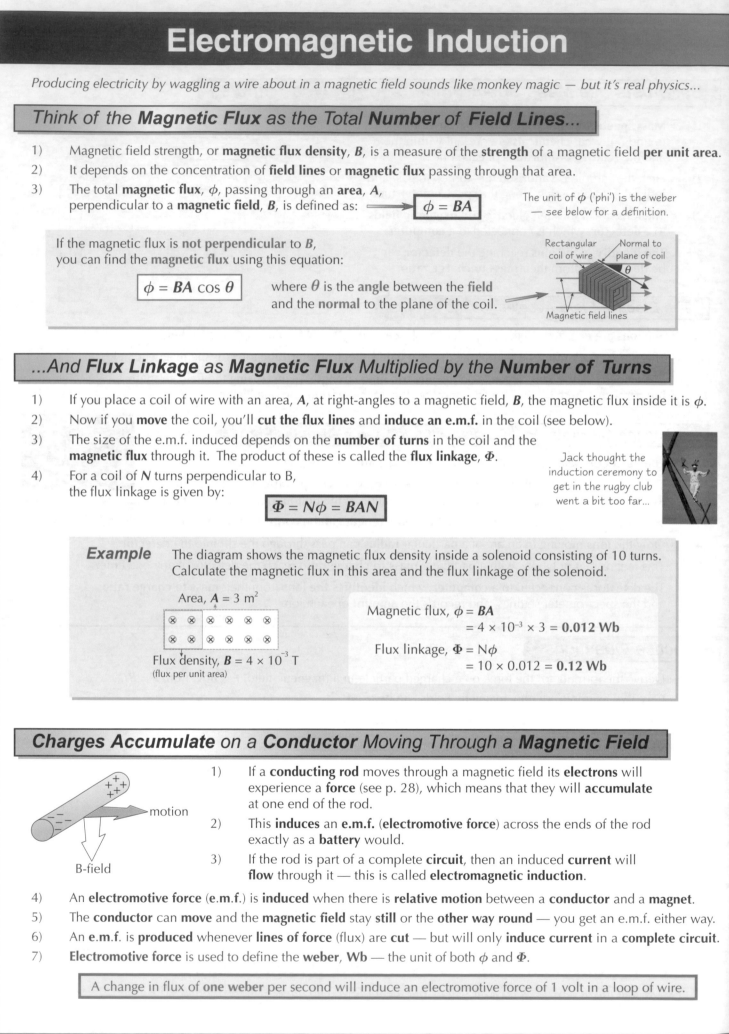

Rectangular coil of wire   Normal to plane of coil

θ

Magnetic field lines

...And **Flux Linkage** as **Magnetic Flux** Multiplied by the **Number of Turns**

1) If you place a coil of wire with an area, **A**, at right-angles to a magnetic field, **B**, the magnetic flux inside it is ϕ.

2) Now if you **move** the coil, you'll **cut the flux lines** and **induce an e.m.f.** in the coil (see below).

3) The size of the e.m.f. induced depends on the **number of turns** in the coil and the **magnetic flux** through it. The product of these is called the **flux linkage**, Φ.

4) For a coil of **N** turns perpendicular to B, the flux linkage is given by:

$$\boxed{\Phi = N\phi = BAN}$$

Jack thought the induction ceremony to get in the rugby club went a bit too far...

Example   The diagram shows the magnetic flux density inside a solenoid consisting of 10 turns. Calculate the magnetic flux in this area and the flux linkage of the solenoid.

Area, **A** = 3 m²

⊗ ⊗ ⊗ ⊗ ⊗ ⊗
⊗ ⊗ ⊗ ⊗ ⊗ ⊗

Flux density, **B** = 4 × 10⁻³ T
(flux per unit area)

Magnetic flux, $\phi = BA$
$= 4 \times 10^{-3} \times 3 = \mathbf{0.012\ Wb}$

Flux linkage, $\Phi = N\phi$
$= 10 \times 0.012 = \mathbf{0.12\ Wb}$

Charges Accumulate on a Conductor Moving Through a Magnetic Field

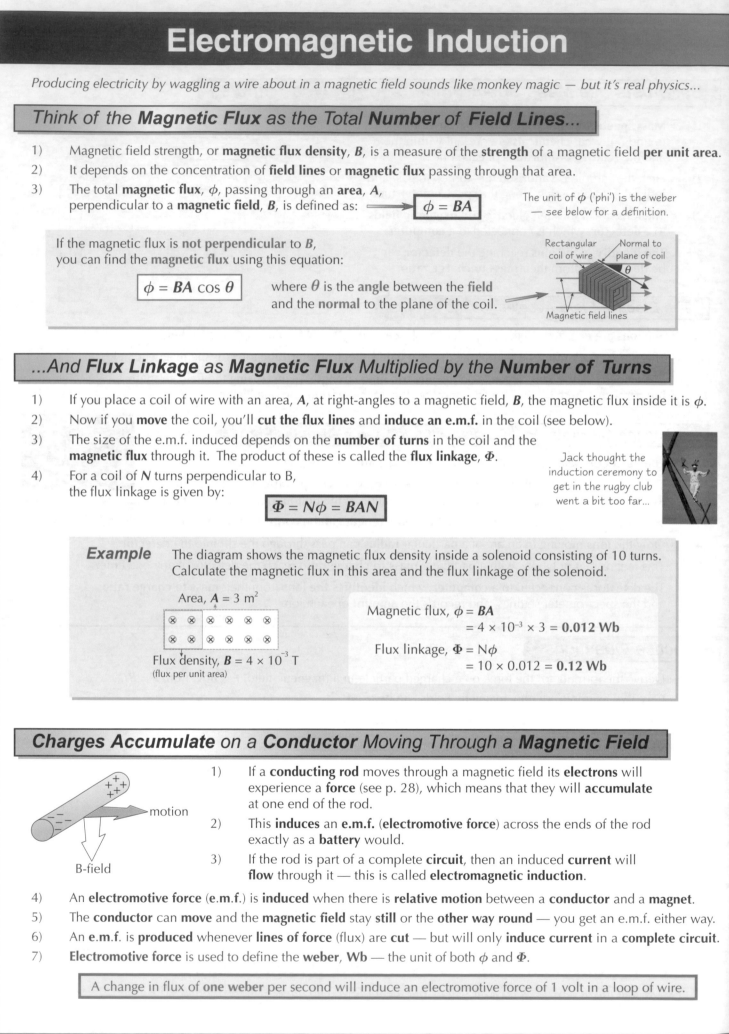

motion

B-field

1) If a **conducting rod** moves through a magnetic field its **electrons** will experience a **force** (see p. 28), which means that they will **accumulate** at one end of the rod.

2) This **induces** an **e.m.f.** (**electromotive force**) across the ends of the rod exactly as a **battery** would.

3) If the rod is part of a complete **circuit**, then an induced **current** will **flow** through it — this is called **electromagnetic induction**.

4) An **electromotive force** (**e.m.f.**) is **induced** when there is **relative motion** between a **conductor** and a **magnet**.

5) The **conductor** can **move** and the **magnetic field** stay **still** or the **other way round** — you get an e.m.f. either way.

6) An **e.m.f.** is **produced** whenever **lines of force** (flux) are **cut** — but will only **induce current** in a **complete circuit**.

7) **Electromotive force** is used to define the **weber**, **Wb** — the unit of both ϕ and Φ.

> A change in flux of **one weber** per second will induce an electromotive force of 1 volt in a loop of wire.

Electromagnetic Induction

These Results are Summed up by *Faraday's Law*...

FARADAY'S LAW: The **induced e.m.f.** is **directly proportional** to the **rate of change of flux linkage**.

1) **Faraday's law** can be written as:

$$\text{Induced e.m.f.} = \frac{\text{flux change}}{\text{time taken}} = \frac{\Delta\Phi}{\Delta t} = N\frac{\Delta\phi}{\Delta t}$$

2) The **size** of the e.m.f. is shown by the **gradient** of a graph of Φ against time.

3) The **area under** the graph of e.m.f. against time gives the **flux change**.

Φ e.m.f. = gradient

time

e.m.f.

Φ = area

time

Example

A conducting rod of **length** l moves a **distance** x through a perpendicular magnetic field.

a) What is the flux cut by the rod in terms of l and x?

$$\phi = BA = Blx$$

motion

b) What is the induced e.m.f. in the rod, in terms of the rod's velocity, v?

$$\text{Induced e.m.f.} = \frac{\text{flux change}}{\text{time taken}} = \frac{Blx}{t} = Blv$$

(since $v = x \div t$)

Exam questions often ask you to calculate the e.m.f. induced by the Earth's magnetic field across the wingspan of a plane. Think of it as a moving rod and use the equation above.

Practice Questions

Q1   What is the difference between magnetic flux density, magnetic flux and magnetic flux linkage?

Q2   State Faraday's law.

Q3   A coil consists of N turns each of area A. If it is placed at right angles to a uniform magnetic field, what is its flux linkage?

Q4   Explain how you can find the direction of an induced e.m.f. in a copper bar moving at right angles to a magnetic field.

Exam Questions

Q1   A coil of area 0.23 m² is placed at right angles to a magnetic field of 2×10^{-3} T.

  (a) What is the magnetic flux passing through the coil?   [2 marks]

  (b) If the coil has 150 turns, what is the magnetic flux linkage in the coil?   [2 marks]

  (c) Over a period of 2.5 seconds the magnetic field is reduced uniformly to 1.5×10^{-3} T.
     What is the size of the e.m.f. induced across the ends of the coil?   [3 marks]

Q2   A 0.01 m² coil of 500 turns is perpendicular to a magnetic field of 0.9 T.

  (a) What is the magnetic flux linkage in the coil?   [2 marks]

  (b) The coil is rotated until the normal to the plane of the coil is at 90° to the direction of the magnetic field.
    The movement is uniform and takes 0.5 s. Calculate the e.m.f. induced by this movement.   [4 marks]

Beware — physics can induce extreme confusion...

OK... I know that might have seemed a bit scary... but the more you go through it, the more it stops being a big scary monster of doom and just becomes another couple of equations you have to remember. Plus it's one of those things that makes you sound well clever... "What did you learn today, Jim?", "Oh, just magnetic flux linkage in solenoids, Mum..."

Electromagnetic Induction

E.m.f. is a bit of a rebel... it always opposes the change that caused it.

The **Direction** of the **Induced E.m.f.** and **Current** are given by **Lenz's Law**

> LENZ'S LAW: The **induced e.m.f.** is always in such a **direction** as to **oppose** the **change** that caused it.

1) **Lenz's law** and **Faraday's law** can be **combined** to give one formula that works for both:

> induced e.m.f. = – rate of change of flux linkage

2) The **minus sign** shows the direction of the **induced e.m.f.**

3) The idea that an induced e.m.f. will **oppose** the change that caused it agrees with the principle of the **conservation of energy** — the **energy used** to pull a conductor through a magnetic field, against the **resistance** caused by magnetic **attraction**, is what **produces** the **induced current**.

4) **Lenz's law** can be used to find the **direction** of an **induced e.m.f.** and **current** in a conductor travelling at right angles to a magnetic field...

1) **Lenz's law** says that the **induced e.m.f.** will produce a force that **opposes** the motion of the conductor — in other words a **resistance**.

2) Using **Fleming's left-hand rule** (see p. 28), point your thumb in the direction of the force of **resistance** — which is in the **opposite direction** to the motion of the conductor.

3) Your **second finger** will now give you the direction of the **induced e.m.f.**

4) If the conductor is **connected** as part of a **circuit**, a current will be induced in the **same direction** as the induced e.m.f.

An **Alternator** is a **Generator** of **Alternating Current**

1) **Generators**, or dynamos, **convert** kinetic energy into **electrical energy** — they **induce** an electric **current** by **rotating** a **coil** in a magnetic field.

2) The diagram shows a simple **alternator** — a generator of **AC**. It has **slip rings** and **brushes** to connect the coil to an external circuit.

3) The output **voltage** and **current** change direction with every **half rotation** of the coil, producing **alternating current** (**AC**).

Transformers Work by Electromagnetic **Induction**

1) **Transformers** are devices that use electromagnetic induction to **change** the size of the **voltage** for an **alternating current**.

2) They consist of **two coils of wire** wrapped around an **iron core**.

3) An alternating current flowing in the **primary** (or input) **coil** produces **magnetic flux** in the **iron core**.

4) The **magnetic field** is passed through the **iron core** to the **secondary** (or output) coil, where it **induces** an alternating **voltage** of the same frequency.

5) The **ratio** of the **number of turns** on each coil along with the voltage across the primary coil determines the **size of the voltage** induced in the secondary coil.

> **Step-up** transformers **increase** the **voltage** by having **more turns** on the **secondary** coil than the primary.
> **Step-down** transformers **reduce** the voltage by having **fewer** turns on the secondary coil.

Electromagnetic Induction

You Can **Calculate** the **Voltage Change** Induced by a **Transformer**

From Faraday's law (page 31), the **induced** e.m.f.s in both the **primary** and **secondary** coils can be calculated:

Primary coil
$$V_p = N_p \frac{\Delta \Phi}{\Delta t}$$

Secondary coil
$$V_s = N_s \frac{\Delta \Phi}{\Delta t}$$

These can be combined to give the equation for an **ideal transformer**:

$$\frac{V_p}{V_s} = \frac{N_p}{N_s}$$

(where N is the number of turns in a coil)

Example   What is the output voltage for a transformer with a primary coil of 100 turns, a secondary coil of 300 turns and an input voltage of 230 V?

$$\frac{V_p}{V_s} = \frac{N_p}{N_s} \Rightarrow \frac{230}{V_s} = \frac{100}{300} \Rightarrow V_s = \frac{230 \times 300}{100} = 690 \text{ V}$$

... robots in disguise

Transformers are an **Important** Part of the **National Grid**

1) **Electricity** from power stations is sent round the country in the **national grid** at the **lowest** possible current, because **losses** due to the **resistance** in the cables are proportional to the current squared.

2) Since **power = current × voltage**, a **low current** means a **high voltage**.

3) **Transformers** allow us to **step up** the voltage to around **400 000 V** for **transmission** through the national grid, and then **reduce** it again to **230 V** for domestic use.

Practice Questions

Q1   State Lenz's law.

Q2   Explain how you can find the direction of an induced e.m.f. in a copper bar moving at right angles to a magnetic field.

Q3   What is the function of an AC generator? Outline how one works.

Q4   Draw a diagram of a simple transformer. What is meant by a step-down transformer?

Exam Questions

Q1   An aeroplane with a wingspan of 30 m flies at a speed of 100 ms⁻¹ perpendicular to the Earth's magnetic field as shown. The Earth's magnetic field at the aeroplane's location is 60×10^{-6} T.

(a) Calculate the induced e.m.f. between the wing-tips.   [2 marks]

(b) Complete the diagram to show the direction of the induced e.m.f. between the wing-tips.   [1 mark]

Q2   A transformer with 150 turns in the primary coil has an input voltage of 9 V.

(a) How many turns are needed in the secondary coil to increase the voltage to 45 V?   [2 marks]

(b) What voltage would be induced in the secondary coil if it consisted of 90 turns?   [2 marks]

(c) What is meant by a step-up transformer?   [1 mark]

Aaaaaand — relax...

Breathe a sigh of relief, pat yourself on the back and make a brew — well done, you've reached the end of the section. That was pretty nasty stuff, but don't let all of those equations get you down — once you've learnt the main ones and can use them blindfolded, even the trickiest looking exam question will be a walk in the park...

Capacitors

Capacitors are things that store electrical charge — like a charge bucket. Sounds simple enough... ha... ha, ha, ha...

Capacitance is Defined as the Amount of Charge Stored per Volt

$$C = \frac{Q}{V}$$

where **Q** is the **charge** in coulombs, **V** is the **potential difference** in volts and **C** is the **capacitance** in farads (F) — 1 farad = 1 C V⁻¹.

A farad is a **huge** unit so you'll usually see capacitances expressed in terms of:

μF — microfarads ($\times 10^{-6}$)

nF — nanofarads ($\times 10^{-9}$)

pF — picofarads ($\times 10^{-12}$)

Capacitors are used in Flash Photography and Nuclear Fusion

Capacitors are found in loads of **electronic devices** — they're useful because they **store** up electric charge for use when you want it. What's more, the **amount of charge** that can be stored and the **rate** at which it's **released** can be controlled by the type of capacitor chosen — for example:

1) **Flash photography** — when you take a picture, charge stored in a **capacitor** flows through a tube of xenon gas which emits a **bright light**. In order to give a **brief flash** of bright light, the capacitor has to discharge really quickly to give a **short pulse** of high current.

2) **Nuclear fusion** — a colossal amount of **energy** is needed to start a nuclear fusion reaction (p. 61) — one way to deliver this is using **lasers** controlled by **capacitors**. The capacitors release a huge charge in a fraction of a second to **maximise** the amount of energy in each pulse of laser-light.

3) **Back-up power supplies** — **computers** are often connected to back-up power supplies to make sure that you don't lose any data if there's a **power cut**. These often use **large capacitors** that store charge while the power is on then release that charge slowly if the power goes off. The capacitors are designed to discharge over a number of hours, maintaining a **steady flow** of charge.

Combined Capacitance Increases in Parallel, but Decreases in Series

1) If you put two or more **capacitors** in a **parallel circuit**, the **p.d.** across each one is the **same**.

2) Each capacitor can store the **same** amount of **charge** as if it was the **only component** in the circuit.

3) So, the **total capacitance** is just the **sum** of the individual capacitances: $\boxed{C_{total} = C_1 + C_2}$

4) When you put capacitors in a **series circuit**, the **p.d.** is **shared** between each one.

5) Each capacitor can only store a **fraction** of the **charge** available, so the **total capacitance** is **less than** the individual capacitances: $\boxed{\dfrac{1}{C_{total}} = \dfrac{1}{C_1} + \dfrac{1}{C_2}}$

You could be asked to solve circuit problems using these equations.

Capacitors Store Energy

1) In this circuit, when the switch is flicked to the **left**, **charge** builds up on the plates of the **capacitor**. **Electrical energy**, provided by the battery, is **stored** by the capacitor.

2) If the switch is flicked to the **right**, the energy stored on the plates will **discharge** through the **bulb**, converting electrical energy into light and heat.

3) **Work** is done **removing charge** from **one plate** and depositing **charge** onto the other one to charge the capacitor. The energy for this must come from the **electrical energy** of the **battery**, and is given by **charge × p.d.** The energy **stored** by a capacitor is **equal** to the **work done** by the **battery**.

4) So, you can find the **energy stored** by the capacitor from the **area** under a **graph** of **p.d.** against **charge stored** on the capacitor. The p.d. across the capacitor is **proportional** to the charge stored on it, so the graph will be a **straight line** through the origin. The **energy stored** is given by the **yellow triangle**.

5) **Area of triangle = ½ × base × height**, so the energy stored by the capacitor is: $\boxed{W = \dfrac{1}{2}QV}$

W stands for 'work done', but you can also use E for energy

You need to remember where this equation comes from.

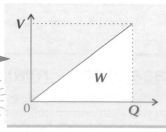

Capacitors

There are **Three** Expressions for the **Energy Stored** by a Capacitor

1) You know the first one already: $W = \frac{1}{2}QV$ ← *W* stands for 'work done', but you can also use *E* for energy

2) $C = \frac{Q}{V}$, so $Q = CV$. Substitute that into the energy equation: $W = \frac{1}{2}CV \times V$. So: $W = \frac{1}{2}CV^2$

3) $V = \frac{Q}{C}$, so $W = \frac{1}{2}Q \times \frac{Q}{C}$. Simplify: $W = \frac{Q^2}{2C}$

Example A 900 µF capacitor is charged up to a potential difference of 240 V. Calculate the energy stored by the capacitor.

First, choose the best equation to use — you've been given **V** and **C**, so you need $W = \frac{1}{2}CV^2$.

Substitute the values in: $E = \frac{1}{2} \times 9 \times 10^{-4} \times 240^2 = 25.92$ J

Practice Questions

Q1 Define capacitance.

Q2 What is the relationship between charge, voltage and capacitance?

Q3 Write the following in standard form: a) 220 µF b) 1000 pF c) 470 nF.

Exam Questions

Q1 Capacitors are found in many electronic devices, including cameras.

(a) Outline how capacitors are used in cameras. [1 mark]

(b) Explain why a capacitor is a suitable component for this use. [2 marks]

Q2 From the graphs below, calculate the capacitance of the capacitor and the charge stored on its plates.

[4 marks]

Q3 A 500 mF capacitor is fully charged up from a 12 V supply.

(a) Calculate the total energy stored by the capacitor. [2 marks]

(b) Calculate the charge stored by the capacitor. [2 marks]

Q4 Explain why a circuit with two 470 mF capacitors in parallel would store more charge than a circuit with two 470 mF capacitors in series, when the same voltage is applied to both circuits.
In your answer, you should make clear the sequence of steps in your argument. [4 marks]

Capacitance — fun, it's not...

Capacitors are really useful in the real world. Pick an appliance, any appliance, and it'll probably have a capacitor or several. If I'm being honest though, the only saving grace of these pages for me is that they're not especially hard...

Charging and Discharging

Charging and discharging — sounds painful...

You can **Charge** a **Capacitor** by Connecting it to a **Battery**

1) When a capacitor is connected to a **battery**, a **current** flows in the circuit until the capacitor is **fully charged**, then **stops**.

2) The electrons flow onto the plate connected to the **negative terminal** of the battery, so a **negative charge** builds up.

3) This build-up of negative charge **repels** electrons off the plate connected to the **positive terminal** of the battery, making that plate positive. These electrons are attracted to the positive terminal of the battery.

4) An **equal** but **opposite** charge builds up on each plate, causing a **potential difference** between the plates. Remember that **no charge** can flow **between** the plates because they're **separated** by an **insulator** (dielectric).

Flow of charge shown by centre zero meter

5) Initially the **current** through the circuit is **high**. But, as **charge** builds up on the plates, **electrostatic repulsion** makes it **harder** and **harder** for more electrons to be deposited. When the p.d. across the **capacitor** is equal to the p.d. across the **battery**, the **current** falls to **zero**. The capacitor is **fully charged**.

an equal but opposite charge

p.d. across capacitor opposes battery p.d.
When p.d.$_{capacitor}$ = p.d.$_{battery}$, no more charge flows.

To **Discharge** a Capacitor, **Take Out** the **Battery** and **Reconnect** the **Circuit**

1) When a **charged capacitor** is connected across a **resistor**, the p.d. drives a **current** through the circuit.

2) This current flows in the **opposite direction** from the **charging current**.

3) The capacitor is **fully discharged** when the **p.d.** across the plates and the **current** in the circuit are both **zero**.

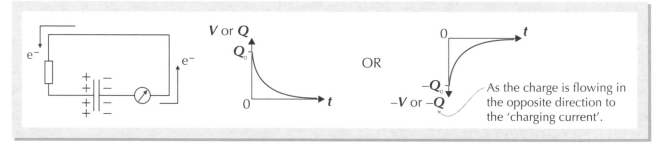

OR

As the charge is flowing in the opposite direction to the 'charging current'.

The **Time Taken** to **Charge** or **Discharge** Depends on **Two Factors**

The **time** it takes to charge up or discharge a capacitor depends on:

1) The **capacitance** of the capacitor (C). This affects the amount of **charge** that can be transferred at a given **voltage**.

2) The **resistance** of the circuit (R). This affects the **current** in the circuit.

Charging and Discharging

The Charge on a Capacitor Decreases Exponentially

1) When a capacitor is **discharging**, the amount of **charge** left on the plates falls **exponentially with time**.

2) That means it always takes the **same length of time** for the charge to **halve**, no matter **how much charge** you start with — like radioactive decay (see p. 48).

The charge left on the plates of a capacitor discharging from full is given by the equation:

$$Q = Q_0 e^{-\frac{t}{CR}}$$

where Q_0 is the charge of the capacitor when it's fully charged.

The graphs of **V** against **t** and **I** against **t** for charging and discharging are also exponential.

charging

$$V = V_0 - V_0 e^{-\frac{t}{CR}}$$

discharging

$$V = V_0 e^{-\frac{t}{CR}}$$

Time Constant τ = CR

τ is the Greek letter 'tau'

If $t = \tau = CR$ is put into the equation above, then $Q = Q_0 e^{-1}$. So when $t = \tau$: $\dfrac{Q}{Q_0} = \dfrac{1}{e}$, where $\dfrac{1}{e} \approx \dfrac{1}{2.718} \approx 0.37$.

1) So τ, the **time constant**, is the time taken for the charge on a discharging capacitor (Q) to **fall to 37%** of Q_0.

2) It's also the time taken for the charge of a charging capacitor to **rise to 63%** of Q_0.

3) The **larger** the **resistor** in series with the capacitor, the **longer it takes** to charge or discharge.

4) In practice, the time taken for a capacitor to charge or discharge **fully** is taken to be about 5**CR**.

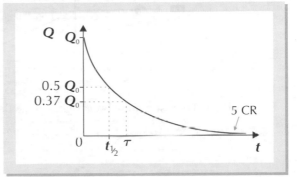

Practice Questions

Q1 Sketch graphs to show the variation of p.d. across the plates of a capacitor with time for:
a) charging a capacitor, b) discharging a capacitor.

Q2 What two factors affect the rate of charge of a capacitor?

Q3 What is meant by the term 'time constant' in relation to capacitors?

Exam Question

Q1 A 250 µF capacitor is fully charged from a 6 V battery and then discharged through a 1 kΩ resistor.

(a) Calculate the time taken for the charge on the capacitor to fall to 37% of its original value. [2 marks]

(b) Calculate the percentage of the total charge remaining on the capacitor after 0.7s. [3 marks]

(c) If the charging voltage is increased to 12 V, what effect will this have on:

i) the total charge stored

ii) the capacitance of the capacitor

iii) the time taken to fully charge [3 marks]

An analogy — consider the lowly bike pump...

A good way to think of the charging process is like pumping air into a bike tyre. To start with, the air goes in easily, but as the pressure in the tyre increases, it gets harder and harder to squeeze any more air in. The tyre's 'full' when the pressure of the air in the tyre equals the pressure of the pump. The analogy works just as well for discharging...

Scattering to Determine Structure

This page covers the history of the atom during the last century — from Thomson's plum pudding to Rutherford's nuclear model and protons and neutrons.

The **Thomson Model** was Popular in the **19th Century**

Until the early 20th century, physicists believed that the atom was a **positively charged globule** with **negatively charged electrons sprinkled** in it. This "**plum pudding**" model of the atom was known as the **Thomson Model.** This all changed in 1909 when the **Rutherford scattering experiment** was done.

In Rutherford's laboratory, **Hans Geiger** and **Ernest Marsden** studied the scattering of **alpha particles** by **thin metal foils**.

Rutherford's Experiment **Disproved** the **Thomson Model**

Rutherford's Scattering Experiment

A **stream of alpha particles** from a radioactive source was fired at **very thin gold foil**. Geiger and Marsden recorded the number of alpha particles **scattered** at different **angles**.

When alpha particles from a radioactive source strike a fluorescent screen a tiny visible flash of light is produced.

If the **Thomson model** was right, all the flashes should have been seen within a **small angle** of the beam.

This <u>wasn't</u> what they saw.

Geiger and Marsden observed that alpha particles occasionally **scatter at angles greater than 90°**. This can only be possible if they're **striking something more massive** than themselves.

Rutherford's **Model** of the **Atom** — **The Nuclear Model**

This experiment led Rutherford to some **important conclusions**:

1) Most of the **fast, charged alpha particles** went **straight through** the gold foil. Therefore the atom is **mostly empty space**.

2) **Some** of the alpha particles are **deflected back** through **significant angles**, so the **centre** of the atom must be **tiny** but contain **a lot of mass**. Rutherford named this the **nucleus**.

3) The **alpha particles** were **repelled**, so the **nucleus** must have **positive charge**.

4) **Atoms** are **neutral overall** so the **electrons** must be on the outside of the atom — separating one atom from the next.

Scattering to Determine Structure

Atoms are made up of Protons, Neutrons and Electrons

Inside **every atom**, there's a **nucleus** containing **protons** and **neutrons**. **Protons** and **neutrons** are both known as **nucleons**. **Orbiting** this core are the **electrons**. This is called the **nuclear model** of the atom.

Although the **proton** and **neutron** are **2000 times** more **massive** than the **electron**, the nucleus only takes up a **tiny proportion** of the atom. The electrons orbit at relatively **vast distances**.

The nucleus is only one **10 000th the size** of the whole atom — most of the atom is **empty space**.

The diagram shows **neutral oxygen**, with **eight protons** and **eight electrons**.

The nucleus — containing protons and neutrons

The electrons in orbit around the nucleus

The Proton Number is the Number of Protons in the Nucleus

No... really.

The **proton number** is sometimes called the **atomic number**, and has the **symbol Z** (don't ask me why). **Z** is just the **number of protons** in the nucleus.

It's the **proton number** that **defines** the **element** — **no two elements** will have the **same** number of protons.

In a **neutral atom**, the number of **electrons equals** the number of **protons**. The element's **reactions** and **chemical behaviour** depend on the number of **electrons**. So the **proton number** tells you a lot about its **chemical properties**.

The Nucleon Number is the Total Number of Protons and Neutrons

The **nucleon number** is also called the **mass number**, and has the **symbol A** (*shrug*). It tells you how many **protons** and **neutrons** are in the nucleus.

Each **proton or neutron** has a **mass** of (approximately) **1 atomic mass unit** (see p.58). The mass of an electron compared with a nucleon is virtually nothing, so the **number** of **nucleons** is about the same as the **atom's mass** (in atomic mass units).

Atomic Structure can be Represented Using Standard Notation

STANDARD NOTATION:

The **proton number** or **atomic number (Z)** — there are six protons in a carbon atom.

$$^{12}_{6}\text{C}$$

The **nucleon number** or **mass number (A)** — there are a total of 12 protons and neutrons in a carbon-12 atom.

The symbol for the element carbon.

Practice Questions

Q1 List the particles that make up the atom and give their charges and relative masses.

Q2 Define the proton number and nucleon number.

Exam Questions

Q1 In 1911, Ernest Rutherford proposed the nuclear model of the atom after experiments using alpha-particle scattering.

(a) Describe the nuclear model of the atom. [3 marks]

(b) Explain how the alpha-particle scattering experiment provided evidence for Rutherford's model. [3 marks]

Q2 How many protons, neutrons and electrons are there in a (neutral) $^{16}_{8}$O atom? [2 marks]

Alpha scattering — it's positively repulsive...

The important things to learn from these two pages are the nuclear model for the structure of the atom (i.e. a large mass nucleus surrounded by orbiting electrons) and how Geiger and Marsden's alpha-particle scattering experiment gives evidence that supports this model. Once you know that, take a deep breath — it's about to get a little more confusing.

Nuclear Radius and Density

The tiny nucleus — such a weird place, but one that you need to become ultra familiar with. Lucky you...

The Nucleus is a Very Small Part of a Whole Atom

1) By **probing atoms** using scattering and diffraction methods, we know that the **diameter of an atom** is about 0.1 nm (1×10^{-10} m) and the diameter of the smallest **nucleus** is about 2 fm (2×10^{-15} m — pronounced "femtometres").

2) So basically, **nuclei** are really, really **tiny** compared with the size of the **whole atom**.

3) To make this **easier to visualise**, try imagining a **large Ferris wheel** (which is pretty darn big) as the size of **an atom**. If you then put a **grain of rice** (which is rather small) in the centre, this would be the size of the atom's **nucleus**.

4) **Molecules** are just a number of **atoms joined together**. As a rough guide, the size of a molecule equals the number of atoms in it multiplied by the size of one atom.

The Nucleus is Made Up of Nucleons

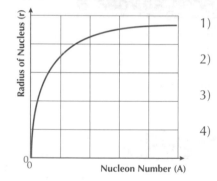

1) The **particles** that make up the nucleus (i.e. **protons** and **neutrons**) are called **nucleons**.

2) The **number of nucleons** in an atom is called the **mass** (or **nucleon**) **number, A**.

3) As **more nucleons** are added to the nucleus, it gets **bigger**.

4) And as we all know by now, you can measure the size of a nucleus by firing particles at it (see p. 40).

See p. 41 for more on the mass number and how this is used to represent atomic structure in standard notation.

Isotopes have the Same Proton Number, but Different Nucleon Numbers

Atoms with the **same number of protons** but **different numbers of neutrons** are called **isotopes**.

Example: Hydrogen has three isotopes — hydrogen, deuterium and tritium

Hydrogen has 1 proton and 0 neutrons.
Deuterium has 1 proton and 1 neutron.
Tritium has 1 proton and 2 neutrons.

Changing the number of **neutrons doesn't affect** the atom's **chemical** properties.

The **number of neutrons** affects the **stability** of the nucleus though (see p. 50).

Unstable nuclei may be **radioactive** (see p. 46).

The Density of Nuclear Matter is Enormous

1) The **volume** that each nucleon (i.e. a **proton** or a **neutron**) takes up in a nucleus is about the **same**.

2) Because protons and neutrons have nearly the **same mass**, it means that all nuclei have a **similar density** (ρ).

3) But nuclear matter is **no ordinary** stuff. Its density is **enormous**. A **teaspoon** of pure nuclear matter would have a mass of about **five hundred million tonnes**. *(Just to make you gasp in awe and wonder, out in space nuclear matter makes up neutron stars, which are several kilometres in diameter.)*

Nuclear Radius and Density

All Elements Have a Similar Nuclear Density

To calculate **nuclear density** you need to know the **mass** and **volume** of the nucleus — and the equation for density:

$$\rho = \frac{m}{V}$$

The symbol for density, ρ, is the Greek letter 'rho'. Its unit is kg m^{-3}.

If you're asked to **estimate nuclear density**, you might have to **work out** the **volume** of the nucleus from its **radius**. So, just assume the nucleus is a sphere and bung the value into the equation:

$$V = \frac{4}{3}\pi r^3$$

Make sure the radius is in m so your volume is in m^3.

The following examples show how **nuclear density** is pretty much the **same**, **regardless of the element**.

Example 1

Work out the density of a carbon nucleus given that has a radius of 3.2×10^{-15} m and a mass of 2.00×10^{-26} kg.

1)   **Volume (V) of the nucleus** $= \frac{4}{3}\pi r^3$

                         $= 1.37 \times 10^{-43}$ m^3

2)   This gives the **density (ρ)** of a carbon nucleus as:

$$\rho = \frac{m}{V} = \frac{2.00 \times 10^{-26}}{1.37 \times 10^{-43}} = 1.46 \times 10^{17} \text{ kg m}^{-3}$$

Example 2

Work out the density of a gold nucleus given that it has a radius of 8.1×10^{-15} m and a mass of 3.27×10^{-25} kg.

1)   **Volume (V) of the nucleus** $= \frac{4}{3}\pi r^3$

                         $= 2.23 \times 10^{-42}$ m^3

2)   This gives the **density (ρ)** of a gold nucleus as:

$$\rho = \frac{m}{V} = \frac{3.27 \times 10^{-25}}{2.23 \times 10^{-42}} = 1.47 \times 10^{17} \text{ kg m}^{-3}$$

Nuclear density is significantly larger than atomic density — this suggests three important facts about the structure of an atom:
  a) Most of an atom's mass is in its nucleus.
  b) The nucleus is small compared to the atom.
  c) An atom must contain a lot of empty space.

You should expect your estimates of nuclear density to come out around 10^{17} kg m^{-3} — if not, there's probably an error in your working

Practice Questions

Q1   What is the approximate size of an atom?

Q2   What are nucleons?

Q3   What is the term for two atoms with the same number of protons, but different numbers of neutrons?

Q4   Explain why the density of ordinary matter is much less than that of nuclear matter.

Exam Questions

Q1   Define the term 'isotope'. Describe the similarities and differences between the properties of two isotopes of the same element.   [3 marks]

Q2   A radium nucleus has a radius of 8.53×10^{-15} m and a mass of 3.75×10^{-25} kg. Estimate the density of the radium nucleus.   [2 marks]

Q3   A sample of pure gold has a density of 19 300 kg m^{-3}. If the density of a gold nucleus is 1.47×10^{17} kg m^{-3}, discuss what this implies about the structure of a gold atom.   [4 marks]

Nuclear and particle physics — heavy stuff...

So the nucleus is a tiny part of the atom that's incredibly dense. The density doesn't change much from element to element, and nuclear stability depends on the number of neutrons. Learn the theory like your own backyard, but don't worry about remembering equations and values — those friendly examiners have popped them in the exam paper for you. How nice...

The Strong Nuclear Force

Keeping the nucleus together requires a lot of effort — a bit like A2 Physics then...

There are **Forces** at Work **Inside** the **Nucleus**...

There are several different **forces** acting on the nucleons in a nucleus. To understand these forces you first need to take a look at the **electrostatic** forces due to the protons' electric charges, and also the **gravitational** forces.

1) The **electrostatic force**

All protons have an equal, **positive electric charge**. So, packed close together inside a nucleus, these protons will **repel** each other. You can work out the size of this **force of repulsion** using **Coulomb's law**. Assuming that two protons are 1×10^{-14} m apart, the force of repulsion F_R will be:

Electrostatic force repels the protons

$$F_R = \frac{1}{4\pi\varepsilon_o}\frac{Q_1 Q_2}{r^2} = \frac{1}{4\pi\left(8.85\times10^{-12}\right)}\frac{\left(1.6\times10^{-19}\right)\left(1.6\times10^{-19}\right)}{\left(1\times10^{-14}\right)^2} = 2.3 \text{ N}$$

In this example: Q_1 and Q_2 are the electric charges on two protons, ε_o is the permittivity of free space, and r is the distance separating the two protons.

2) The **gravitational force**

Newton's law of gravitation says that two **massive** objects will **attract** each other. So, for the same two protons, this **attractive force**, F_A, will be:

Gravitational force attracts the protons

$$F_A = -G\frac{m_1 m_2}{r^2} = -\left(6.67\times10^{-11}\right)\cdot\frac{\left(1.67\times10^{-27}\right)\left(1.67\times10^{-27}\right)}{\left(1\times10^{-14}\right)^2} = -1.86\times10^{-36}\text{ N}$$

In this example: G is the gravitational constant, m_1 and m_2 are the masses of two protons, and r is the distance separating the two protons.

The **electrostatic force** of repulsion is far **bigger** than the **gravitational** attractive force. If these were the only forces acting in the nucleus, the nucleons would **fly apart**. So there must be **another attractive force** that **holds the nucleus together** — called the **strong nuclear force**. (The gravitational force is so small, it's usually ignored.)

The **Strong Nuclear Force** Binds Nucleons Together

Now pay attention please. This bit's rather strange because the **strong nuclear force** is quite **complicated**, but here are the **main points**:

1) To **hold the nucleus together**, the strong nuclear force must be an **attractive force** that is **larger** than the electrostatic force.

2) Experiments have shown that the strong nuclear force between nucleons has a **short range**. It can only hold nucleons together when they are separated by up to **10 fm** — which is the maximum size of a nucleus.

3) The **strength** of the strong nuclear force between nucleons **quickly falls** beyond this distance (see the graph on the next page).

4) Experiments also show that the strong nuclear force **works equally between all nucleons**. This means that the size of the force is the same whether proton-proton, neutron-neutron or proton-neutron.

5) At **very small separations**, the strong nuclear force must be **repulsive** — otherwise there would be nothing to stop it **crushing** the nucleus to a **point**.

lime green, orange and day-glow pink — repulsive at small separations

The Strong Nuclear Force

The **Size** of the Strong Nuclear Force **Varies** with **Nucleon Separation**

The **strong nuclear force** can be plotted on a **graph** to show how it changes with the **distance of separation** between **nucleons**. If the **electrostatic force** is also plotted, you can see the **relationship** between these **two forces**.

3 The **electrostatic repulsive** force extends over a much **larger range** (indefinitely, actually).

1 The strong nuclear force is **repulsive** for **very small** separations of nucleons.

2 As nucleon separation **increases past about 0.5 fm**, the **strong nuclear force** becomes **attractive**. It reaches a maximum attractive value and then **falls rapidly** towards zero after about **3 fm**.

Practice Questions

Q1   What causes an electrostatic force inside the nucleus?

Q2   Explain why the gravitational forces between nucleons are usually ignored.

Q3   What evidence suggests the existence of a strong nuclear force?

Q4   Is the strong interaction attractive or repulsive at a nucleon separation of 10 fm?

Exam Questions

Q1   Coulomb's law can be used to find the electrostatic force of repulsion between two protons in a nucleus.

$$F = \frac{1}{4\pi\varepsilon_o} \frac{Q_1 Q_2}{r^2}$$

The charge, Q, on a proton is $+1.6 \times 10^{-19}$ C and the permittivity of free space, ε_0, is 8.85×10^{-12} Fm^{-1}.

(a) If two protons are separated by a distance, r, of 9×10^{-15} m, calculate the electrostatic force between them.   [2 marks]
(b) If the protons move closer together, what effect will this have on the repulsive force?   [1 mark]
(c) What is the electrostatic force between a proton and a neutron? Explain your answer.   [2 marks]

Q2   The strong nuclear force binds the nucleus together.
(a) Explain why the force must be repulsive at very short distances.   [1 mark]
(b) How does the strong interaction limit the size of a stable nucleus?   [2 marks]

The strong interaction's like nuclear glue...

Right then, lots of scary looking stuff on these pages, but DON'T PANIC... the important bits can be condensed into a few points: a) the electrostatic force pushes protons in the nucleus apart, b) the strong interaction pulls all nucleons together, c) there's a point where these forces are balanced — this is the typical nucleon separation in a nucleus. Easy eh?...

Radioactive Emissions

Despite its best intentions, the strong force can't always hold nuclei together — instead you get radioactive emissions.

Unstable Atoms are Radioactive

1) If an atom is **unstable**, it will **break down** to **become** more stable. Its **instability** could be caused by having **too many neutrons**, **not enough neutrons**, or just **too much energy** in the nucleus.

2) The atom **decays** by **releasing energy** and/or **particles**, until it reaches a **stable form** — this is called **radioactive decay**.

3) An individual radioactive decay is **random** — it can't be predicted.

There are Four Types of Nuclear Radiation

You need to know all about the **four** different types of **nuclear radiation** — here's a handy **table** to get you started.

Radiation	Symbol	Constituent	Relative Charge	Mass (u)
Alpha	α	A helium nucleus — 2 protons & 2 neutrons	+2	4
Beta-minus (Beta)	β or β⁻	Electron	-1	(negligible)
Beta-plus	β⁺	Positron	+1	(negligible)
Gamma	γ	Short-wavelength, high-frequency electromagnetic wave.	0	0

u stands for atomic mass unit — see p. 58.

See p. 54 for more on positrons.

The Different Types of Radiation have Different Penetrations

Alpha, **beta** and **gamma** radiation can be **fired** at a **variety of objects** with **detectors** placed the **other side** to see whether they **penetrate** the object. You can use an **experiment** like this to **identify** a type of radiation.

When a radioactive particle **hits** an **atom** it can **knock off electrons**, creating an **ion** — so, **radioactive emissions** are also known as **ionising radiation**. The **different types** of radiation have **different ionising power** — there's more detail about this on the next page.

Skin or paper stops ALPHA

Many cm lead stops GAMMA

Thin mica

Few mm aluminium stops BETA

Radiation	Symbol	Ionising	Speed	Penetrating power	Affected by magnetic field
Alpha	α	Strongly	Slow	Absorbed by paper or a few cm of air	Yes
Beta-minus (Beta)	β or β⁻	Weakly	Fast	Absorbed by ~3 mm of aluminium	Yes
Beta-plus	β⁺	Annihilated by electron — so virtually zero range			
Gamma	γ	Very weakly	Speed of light	Absorbed by many cm of lead, or several m of concrete.	No

Radioactive Emissions

Radioactive Isotopes Have Many Uses

Radioactive substances are extremely useful. You can use them for all sorts — to **date** organic material, diagnose **medical problems**, **sterilise** food, and in **smoke alarms**.

Radiocarbon Dating
The radioactive isotope **carbon-14** is used in **radiocarbon dating**. Living plants take in carbon dioxide from the atmosphere as part of **photosynthesis**, including the **radioactive isotope carbon-14**. When they die, the **activity** of carbon-14 in the plant starts to **fall**, with a **half-life** of around **5730 years**. Archaeological finds made from once living material (like wood) can be tested to find the **current amount** of carbon-14 in them, and date them.

Smoke Detectors
Smoke detectors have a **weak** source of α-**radiation** close to **two electrodes**. The radiation **ionises** the air, and a **current** flows between the electrodes. If there's a fire, **smoke absorbs** the **radiation** — the **current stops** and the **alarm sounds**.

Alpha and Beta Particles have Different Ionising Properties

What a **radioactive source** can be **used** for often depends on its **ionising properties**.

1) **Alpha** particles are **strongly positive** — so they can **easily pull electrons** off atoms, **ionising** them.

2) Ionising an atom **transfers** some of the **energy** from the **alpha particle** to the **atom**. The alpha particle **quickly ionises** many atoms (about 10 000 ionisations per alpha particle) and **loses** all its **energy**. This makes alpha-sources suitable for use in **smoke alarms** because they allow **current** to flow, but won't **travel very far**.

3) The **beta**-minus particle has **lower mass** and **charge** than the alpha particle, but a **higher speed**. This means it can still **knock electrons** off atoms. Each **beta** particle will ionise about 100 atoms, **losing energy** at each interaction.

4) This **lower** number of **interactions** means that beta radiation causes much **less damage** to body tissue than alpha radiation. This means beta radiation can be used in **medicine** to target and damage **cancerous cells** — since it passes through healthy tissue without causing too many problems.

5) Gamma radiation is even more **weakly ionising** than beta radiation, so will do even **less damage** to body tissue. This means it can be used for **diagnostic techniques** in medicine — see pages 68-69 for more info.

Practice Questions

Q1 What makes an atom radioactive?

Q2 What are the four types of nuclear radiation? What does each one consist of?

Q3 Which type of radiation is the most penetrating? Which is the most ionising?

Q4 Suggest two uses of nuclear radiation.

Exam Questions

Q1 Briefly describe an absorption experiment to distinguish between alpha, beta and gamma radiation. You may wish to include a sketch in your answer. [4 marks]

Q2 Radioactive isotopes are found in smoke alarms.
(a) Explain the function of radioactive isotopes in smoke alarms. [3 marks]
(b) What type of radiation is emitted by the isotopes in smoke alarms? Explain why this is suitable. [3 marks]

Radioactive emissions — as easy as α, β, γ...

You need to learn the different types of radiation and their properties. Remember that alpha particles are by far the most ionising and so cause more damage if they get inside your body than the same dose of any other radiation — which is one reason we don't use alpha sources as medical tracers. Learn this all really well, then go and have a brew and a bickie...

Exponential Law of Decay

Oooh look — some maths. Good.

Every Isotope *Decays* at a *Different Rate*

1) **Radioactive decay** is completely **random**. You **can't predict which** atom will decay **when**.

2) Although you can't predict the decay of an **individual atom**, if you take a **very large number of atoms**, their **overall behaviour** shows a **pattern**.

3) Any sample of a particular **isotope** (page 42) has the **same rate of decay**, i.e. the same **proportion** of atoms will **decay** in a **given time**.

It could be you.

The *Rate of Decay* is Measured by the *Decay Constant*

The **activity** of a sample — the **number** of atoms that **decay each second** — is **proportional** to the **size of the sample**. For a **given isotope**, a sample **twice** as big would give **twice** the **number of decays** per second.

The **decay constant** (λ) measures how **quickly** an isotope will **decay** — the **bigger** the value of λ, the faster the rate of decay. Its unit is **s^{-1}**.

> activity = decay constant × number of atoms

Or in symbols: $A = \lambda N$ ← *Don't get λ confused with wavelength.*

Activity is measured in **becquerels** (Bq): | 1 Bq = 1 decay per second (s^{-1})

You Need to *Learn* the *Definition of Half-Life*

> The **half-life** ($T_{1/2}$) of an **isotope** is the **average time** it takes for the **number of undecayed atoms** to **halve**.

Measuring the **number of undecayed atoms** isn't the easiest job in the world. **In practice**, half-life isn't measured by counting atoms, but by measuring the **time it takes** the **activity** to **halve**.

The **longer** the **half-life** of an isotope, the **longer** it stays **radioactive**.

The *Number* of *Undecayed* Particles Decreases Exponentially

You **can't** tell when any **one particle** is going to **decay**, but you can **predict** how many particles are left to decay using a **graph** like the one below. The number of **undecayed** particles of an isotope always **decreases exponentially**.

You can even use the **graph** to find the **half-life**.

How to find the half-life of an isotope

STEP 1: Read off the value of count rate, particles or activity when t = 0.

STEP 2: Go to half the original value.

STEP 3: Draw a horizontal line to the curve, then a vertical line down to the x-axis.

STEP 4: Read off the half-life where the line crosses the x-axis.

STEP 5: Check the units carefully.

STEP 6: It's always a good idea to check your answer. Repeat steps 1-4 for a quarter the original value. Divide your answer by two. That will also give you the half-life. Check that you get the same answer both ways.

The half-life stays the same. It takes the same amount of time for half of the atoms to decay regardless of the number of atoms you start with.

The number of atoms approaches zero.

When you're **measuring** the **activity** and **half-life** of a **source**, you've got to **remember background radiation**. The **background radiation** needs to be **subtracted** from the **activity readings** to give the **source activity**.

You'd be **more likely** to actually meet a **count rate-time graph** or an **activity-time graph**. They're both **exactly the same shape** as the graph above, but with **different y-axes**.

Exponential Law of Decay

You Need to Know the Equations for Half-Life and Decay...

1) The number of radioactive nuclei decaying per second (**activity**) is proportional to the number of nuclei remaining.

2) The **half-life** can be **calculated** using the equation:
(where ln is the natural log)

$$T_{\frac{1}{2}} = \frac{\ln 2}{\lambda} \simeq \frac{0.693}{\lambda}$$

3) The **number of radioactive atoms** remaining, **N**, depends on the **number originally** present, **N_o**. The **number remaining** can be calculated using the equation:

$$N = N_0 e^{-\lambda t}$$

Here t = time, measured in seconds.

4) As a sample decays, its activity goes down — there's an equation for that too:

$$A = A_0 e^{-\lambda t}$$

Example:
A sample of the radioactive isotope ^{13}N contains 5×10^6 atoms. The decay constant for this isotope is 1.16×10^{-3} s^{-1}.

a) What is the half-life for this isotope?

$$T_{\frac{1}{2}} = \frac{\ln 2}{1.16 \times 10^{-3}} = 598 \text{ s}$$

b) How many atoms of ^{13}N will remain after 800 seconds?

$$N = N_0 e^{-\lambda t} = 5 \times 10^6 e^{-(1.16 \times 10^{-3})(800)} = 1.98 \times 10^6 \text{ atoms}$$

Capacitors and Radioactive Isotopes Have Similar Decay Equations

Radioactive isotopes might seem very different from **capacitors** in C-R circuits (see page 39), but their **decay equations** are actually **very similar**. This **table** shows the **similarities** and **differences** between the equations.

	Discharging Capacitors	Radioactive Isotopes
1)	Decay equation is $Q = Q_0 e^{-t/CR}$.	Decay equation is $N = N_0 e^{-\lambda t}$.
2)	The **quantity** that decays is Q, the amount of charge left on the plates of the capacitor.	The **quantity** that decays is N, the number of unstable nuclei remaining.
3)	**Initially**, the charge on the plates is Q_0.	**Initially**, the number of nuclei is N_0.
4)	It takes CR seconds for the amount of charge remaining to fall to **37% of its initial value**.	It takes $1/\lambda$ seconds for the number of nuclei remaining to fall to **37% of the initial value**.
5)	The time taken for the amount of charge left to decay by half (the **half-life**) is $t_{\frac{1}{2}} = \ln 2 \times CR$.	The time taken for the number of nuclei to decay by half (the **half-life**) is $t_{\frac{1}{2}} = \ln 2 / \lambda$.

Practice Questions

Q1 Define radioactive activity. What units is it measured in?

Q2 Sketch a general radioactive decay graph showing the number of particles against time.

Q3 What is meant by the term 'half-life'?

Exam Questions

Q1 Explain what is meant by the random nature of radioactive decay. [1 mark]

Q2 You take a reading of 750 Bq from a pure radioactive source. The radioactive source initially contains 50 000 atoms, and background activity in your lab is measured as 50 Bq.
   (a) Calculate the decay constant for your sample. [3 marks]
   (b) What is the half-life of this sample? [2 marks]
   (c) Approximately how many atoms of the radioactive source will there be after 300 seconds? [2 marks]

Radioactivity is a random process — just like revision shouldn't be...

Remember the shape of that graph — whether it's count rate, activity or number of atoms plotted against time, the shape's always the same. This is all pretty straightforward mathsy-type stuff: plugging values in equations, reading off graphs, etc. Not very interesting, though. Ah well, give it a few pages and you might just be longing for a bit of boredom.

Nuclear Decay

The stuff on these pages covers the most important facts about nuclear decay that you're just going to have to make sure you know inside out. I'd be very surprised if you didn't get a question about it in your exam...

Some Nuclei are **More Stable** than Others

The nucleus is under the **influence** of the **strong nuclear force holding** it **together** and the **electromagnetic force pushing** the **protons apart**. It's a very **delicate balance**, and it's easy for a nucleus to become **unstable**. You can get a stability graph by plotting **Z** (atomic number) against **N** (number of neutrons).

A nucleus will be **unstable** if it has:

1) **too many neutrons**
2) **too few neutrons**
3) **too many nucleons** altogether, i.e. it's **too heavy**
4) **too much energy**

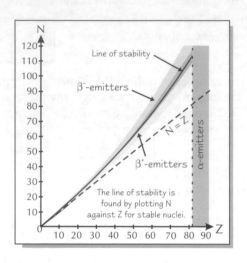

You Can **Represent Nuclear Decay** Using **Equations**

Don't panic — 'nuclear decay equations' sounds a lot more complicated than it really is. You just write down what you **start** off with on the **left**, stick a big **arrow** in the middle, then put the bits you **end** up with on the **right** — easy.

You usually write the particles in **standard notation** (see page 41) so you can see exactly what happens to the **protons** and **neutrons**.

For example, the decay of americium-241 to neptunium-237 looks like this:

$$^{241}_{95}Am \longrightarrow\ ^{237}_{93}Np + ^{4}_{2}\alpha$$

α Emission Happens in **Heavy Nuclei**

When an alpha particle is **emitted**: nucleon number decreases by 4

The **proton number decreases** by **two**, and the **nucleon number decreases** by **four**.

$$^{238}_{92}U \longrightarrow\ ^{234}_{90}Th + ^{4}_{2}\alpha + ^{0}_{0}\nu_e$$

proton number decreases by 2

1) **Alpha emission** only happens in **very heavy** atoms (with more than 82 protons), like **uranium** and **radium**.
2) The **nuclei** of these atoms are **too massive** to be stable.
3) An alpha particle and a **neutrino** (ν_e) are emitted (see p. 53).

β⁻ Emission Happens in **Neutron Rich** Nuclei

1) **Beta-minus** (usually just called beta) decay is the emission of an **electron** from the **nucleus** along with an **antineutrino** (see p. 54).
2) Beta decay happens in isotopes that are **"neutron rich"** (i.e. have many more **neutrons** than **protons** in their nucleus).
3) When a nucleus ejects a beta particle, one of the **neutrons** in the nucleus is **changed** into a **proton**.

In **beta-plus emission**, a **proton** gets **changed** into a **neutron**. The **proton number decreases** by **one**, and the **nucleon number stays the same**.

When a beta-minus particle is **emitted**: nucleon number stays the same

The **proton number increases** by **one**, and the **nucleon number stays the same**.

$$^{188}_{75}Re \longrightarrow\ ^{188}_{76}Os + ^{0}_{-1}\beta + ^{0}_{0}\overline{\nu}_e$$

proton number increases by 1

Nuclear Decay

γ Radiation is Emitted from Nuclei with Too Much Energy

Gamma rays can be emitted from a nucleus with **excess energy** — it's **excited**. This energy is **lost** by emitting a **gamma ray**. This often happens after an **alpha** or **beta** decay.

> The artificial isotope <u>technetium-99^m</u> is formed in an <u>excited state</u>. It is used as a tracer in medical imaging (see p 74).

> During **gamma emission**, there is **no change** to the nuclear **constituents** — the nucleus just **loses excess energy**.

There are Conservation Rules in Nuclear Reactions

In every nuclear reaction **energy**, **momentum**, **proton number / charge** and **nucleon number** must be conserved.

For example, if a **nucleus** has **92 protons** before it decays, then the **decay products** must have **92 protons** between them — it's that simple.

238 = 234 + 4 — nucleon numbers balance

$$^{238}_{92}U \longrightarrow\ ^{234}_{90}Th +\ ^{4}_{2}\alpha$$

92 = 90 + 2 — proton numbers balance

Mass is Not Conserved

1) The **mass** of the **alpha particle** is less than the **individual masses** of **two protons** and **two neutrons**. The difference is called the **mass defect** (see page 58).

2) Mass **doesn't** have to be **conserved** because of **Einstein's equation**: $$E = mc^2$$

3) This says that **mass and energy** are **equivalent**. The **energy released** when the nucleons **bonded together** accounts for the missing mass — so the **energy released** is the same as the **mass defect × c^2**.

Cecil was proud of his ability to conserve mass.

Practice Questions

Q1 What makes a nucleus unstable? Describe the changes that happen in the nucleus during alpha, beta and gamma decay.

Q2 Explain the circumstances in which gamma radiation may be emitted.

Q3 Define the mass defect.

Exam Questions

Q1 (a) Radium-226 undergoes alpha decay to radon. Complete the balanced nuclear equation for this reaction.

$$^{226}_{88}Ra \rightarrow\quad Rn +$$

[3 marks]

(b) Potassium-40 ($Z = 19$, $A = 40$) undergoes beta decay to calcium.
Write a balanced nuclear equation for this reaction.

[3 marks]

Q2 Calculate the energy released during the formation of an alpha particle, given that the total mass of two protons and two neutrons is 6.695×10^{-27} kg, the mass of an alpha particle is 6.645×10^{-27} kg and the speed of light, c, is 3.00×10^8 ms^{-1}.

[3 marks]

Nuclear decay — it can be enough to make you unstable...

$E = mc^2$ is an important equation that says mass and energy are equivalent. Remember it well, 'cos you're going to come across it a lot in questions about mass defect and the energy released in nuclear reactions over the next few pages...

Classification of Particles

There are loads of different types of particle apart from the ones you get in normal matter (protons, neutrons, etc.).
They only appear in cosmic rays and in particle accelerators, and they often decay very quickly, so they're difficult to get
a handle on. Nonetheless, you need to learn about a load of them and their properties.
Don't expect to really understand this (I don't) — you only need to learn it. Stick with it — you'll get there.

Hadrons *are* Particles *that Feel the* Strong Interaction *(e.g. Protons and Neutrons)*

1) The **nucleus** of an atom is made up from **protons** and **neutrons** held together by the **strong nuclear force** (sometimes called the strong interaction) — see p. 44.

2) **Not all particles** can **feel** the **strong interaction** — the ones that **can** are called **hadrons**.

3) Hadrons aren't **fundamental** particles. They're made up of **smaller particles** called **quarks** (see page 56).

4) There are **two** types of **hadron** — **baryons** and **mesons**.

Protons *and* Neutrons *are* Baryons

1) It's helpful to think of **protons** and **neutrons** as **two versions** of the **same particle** — the **nucleon**. They just have **different electric charges**.

2) As well as **protons** and **neutrons**, there are **other baryons** that you don't get in normal matter — like **sigmas** (Σ) — they're **short-lived** and you **don't** need to **know about them** for A2 (woohoo!).

The Proton *is the* Only Stable Baryon

All baryons except protons decay to a **proton**.
Most physicists think that protons don't **decay**.

~ Some theories predict that protons should decay with a very long half-life of about 10^{32} years — but there's no experimental evidence for it at the moment. ~

Baryon and Meson felt the strong interaction.

The Number of Baryons *in a reaction is called the* Baryon Number

Baryon number is the number of baryons. (A bit like **nucleon number** but including unusual baryons like Σ too.)
The **proton** and the **neutron** each have a baryon number **B = +1**.
The **total baryon number** in **any** particle reaction **never changes**.

The Mesons *You Need to Know About are* Pions *and* Kaons

1) **All mesons** are **unstable** and have **baryon number B = 0** (because they're not baryons).

2) **Pions** (π-mesons) are the **lightest mesons**. You get **three versions** with different **electric charges** — π^+, π^0 and π^-. Pions were **discovered** in **cosmic rays**. You get **loads** of them in **high energy particle collisions** like those studied at the **CERN** particle accelerator.

3) **Kaons** (**K**-mesons) are **heavier** and more **unstable** than **pions**. You get different ones like **K⁺**, **K⁻** and **K⁰**.

4) Mesons **interact** with **baryons** via the **strong interaction**.

~ Pion interactions swap p's with n's and n's with p's, but leave the overall baryon number unchanged. ~

Summary *of* Hadron Properties

DON'T PANIC *if you don't understand*

all this yet. For now, just **learn** these properties.
You'll need to work through to the end of page 57
to see how it **all fits in**.

Classification of Particles

Leptons Don't *feel* the **Strong Interaction** (e.g. Electrons and Neutrinos)

1) **Leptons** are **fundamental particles** and they **don't** feel the **strong interaction**.
The only way they can **interact** with other particles is via the **weak interaction**
and gravity (and the electromagnetic force as well if they're charged).

2) **Electrons (e⁻)** are **stable** and very **familiar** but — you guessed it — there are also
two more leptons called the **muon (μ⁻)** and the **tau (τ⁻)** that are just like **heavy electrons**.

3) **Muons** and **taus** are **unstable**, and **decay** eventually into **ordinary electrons**.

4) The **electron**, **muon** and **tau** each come with their **own neutrino**: ν_e, ν_μ and ν_τ.

ν is the Greek letter "nu".

5) **Neutrinos** have **zero** or **almost zero mass** and **zero electric charge** — so they don't do much.
Neutrinos only take part in **weak interactions** (see p. 57). In fact, a neutrino can **pass right
through the Earth** without **anything** happening to it.

You Have to **Count** the **Three Types** of Lepton **Separately**

Each lepton is given a **lepton
number** of **+1**, but the **electron,
muon** and **tau** types of lepton have
to be **counted separately**.

You get **three different** lepton
numbers: L_e, L_μ and L_τ.

*Like the baryon number, the
lepton number is just the
number of leptons.*

Name	Symbol	Charge	L_e	L_μ	L_τ
electron	e^-	−1	+1	0	0
electron neutrino	ν_e	0	+1	0	0
muon	μ^-	−1	0	+1	0
muon neutrino	ν_μ	0	0	+1	0
tau	τ	−1	0	0	+1
tau neutrino	ν_τ	0	0	0	+1

Neutrons Decay into Protons

The **neutron** is an **unstable particle** that **decays** into a **proton**. (But it's much more stable when it's part of a nucleus.)
It's really just an **example** of β⁻ decay, which is caused by the **weak interaction**.

$$n \rightarrow p + e^- + \bar{\nu}_e$$

*Free neutrons (i.e. ones not held in a
nucleus) have a half-life of about 15 minutes.*

The antineutrino has L_e = –1 so the total lepton number is zero.
Antineutrino? Yes, well I haven't mentioned antiparticles yet.
Just wait for the next page ...

Practice Questions

Q1 List the differences between a hadron and a lepton.

Q2 Which is the only stable baryon?

Q3 A particle collision at CERN produces 2 protons, 3 pions and 1 neutron.
What is the total baryon number of these particles?

Q4 Which two particles have lepton number L_τ = +1?

Exam Questions

Q1 List all the decay products of the neutron. Explain why this decay cannot be due to the strong interaction. [3 marks]

Q2 Initially the muon was incorrectly identified as a meson. Explain why the muon is not a meson. [3 marks]

Go back to the top of page 52 — do not pass GO, do not collect £200...

*Do it. Go back and read it again. I promise — read these pages about 3 or 4 times and you'll start to see a pattern.
There are hadrons that feel the force, leptons that don't. Hadrons are either baryons or mesons, and they're all weird
except for those well-known baryons: protons and neutrons. There are loads of leptons, including good old electrons.*

Antiparticles

More stuff that seems to laugh in the face of common sense — but actually, antiparticles help to explain a lot in particle physics... (Oh, and if you haven't read pages 52 and 53 yet then go back and read them now — no excuses, off you go...)

Antiparticles were Predicted Before they were Discovered

When **Paul Dirac** wrote down an equation obeyed by **electrons**, he found a kind of **mirror image** solution.

1) It predicted the existence of a particle like the **electron** but with **opposite electric charge** — the **positron**.

2) The **positron** turned up later in a cosmic ray experiment. Positrons are **antileptons** so $L_e = -1$ for them. They have **identical mass** to electrons but they carry a **positive** charge.

Nice one Paul. Now we've got twice as many things to worry about.

Every Particle has an Antiparticle

Each particle type has a **corresponding antiparticle** with the **same mass** but with **opposite charge**. For instance, an **antiproton** is a **negatively charged** particle with the same mass as the **proton**.

Even the shadowy **neutrino** has an antiparticle version called the **antineutrino** — it doesn't do much either.

Particle	Symbol	Charge	B	L_e	Antiparticle	Symbol	Charge	B	L_e
proton	p	+1	+1	0	antiproton	$\bar{p}$	−1	−1	0
neutron	n	0	+1	0	antineutron	$\bar{n}$	0	−1	0
electron	e	−1	0	+1	positron	e^+	+1	0	−1
electron neutrino	ν_e	0	0	+1	electron antineutrino	$\bar{\nu}_e$	0	0	−1

You can Create Matter and Antimatter from Energy

You've probably heard about the **equivalence** of energy and mass. It all comes out of Einstein's special theory of relativity. **Energy** can turn into **mass** and **mass** can turn into **energy** if you know how — all you need is one fantastic and rather famous formula.

$$E = mc^2$$

It's a good thing this doesn't randomly happen all the time or else you could end up with cute bunny rabbits popping up and exploding unexpectedly all over the place. Oh, the horror...

As you've probably guessed, there's a bit **more to it** than that:

> When **energy** is converted into **mass** you have to make **equal amounts** of **matter** and **antimatter**.

Fire **two protons** at each other at high speed and you'll end up with a lot of **energy** at the point of impact. This energy can form **more particles**.

If an extra **proton** is created, there has to be an **antiproton** made to go with it. It's called **pair production**.

Antiparticles

Each **Particle-Antiparticle Pair** is Produced from a **Single Photon**

Pair production only happens if **one gamma ray photon** has enough energy to produce that much mass. It also tends to happen near a **nucleus**, which helps conserve momentum.

You usually get **electron-positron** pairs produced (rather than any other pair) — because they have a relatively **low mass**.

The particle tracks are curved because there's usually a magnetic field present in particle physics experiments. They curve in opposite directions because of the opposite charges on the electron and positron.

The **Opposite** of **Pair Production** is **Annihilation**

When a **particle** meets its **antiparticle** the result is **annihilation**. All the **mass** of the particle and antiparticle gets converted to **energy**. In ordinary matter antiparticles can only exist for a fraction of a second before this happens, so you won't see many of them.

The electron and positron annihilate and their mass is converted into the energy of a pair of gamma ray photons.

Mesons are Their **Own Antiparticles**

Just before you leave this bit it's worth mentioning that the π^- meson is just the **antiparticle** of the π^+ meson, and the **antiparticle** of a π^0 meson is **itself**. You'll see why on p. 56. So we don't need any more particles here... Phew.

(If you don't know what a meson is, look back at page 52.)

Practice Questions

Q1   Which antiparticle has zero charge and a baryon number of –1?

Q2   Describe the properties of an electron antineutrino.

Q3   What is pair production? What happens when a proton collides with an antiproton?

Exam Questions

Q1   Write down an equation for the reaction between a positron and an electron and give the name for this type of reaction.   [2 marks]

Q2   According to Einstein, mass and energy are equivalent. Explain why the mass of a block of iron cannot be converted directly into energy.   [2 marks]

Q3   Give a reason why the reaction $p + p \rightarrow p + p + n$ is not possible.   [1 mark]

Now stop meson around and do some work...

The idea of every particle having an antiparticle might seem a bit strange, but just make sure you know the main points — a) if energy is converted into a particle, you also get an antiparticle, b) an antiparticle won't last long before it bumps into the right particle and annihilates it with a big ba-da-boom, c) this releases the energy it took to make them to start with...

Quarks

*If you haven't read pages 52 to 55, do it now! For the rest of you — here are the **juicy bits** you've been waiting for. Particle physics makes **a lot more sense** when you look at quarks. More sense than it did before anyway.*

Quarks are Fundamental Particles

Quarks are the **building blocks** for **hadrons** (baryons and mesons).

If that first sentence doesn't make much sense to you, read pages 52-55 — you have been warned... twice.

1) To make **protons** and **neutrons** you only need two types of quark — the **up** quark (**u**) and the **down** quark (**d**).

2) An extra one called the **strange** quark (**s**) lets you make more particles with a property called **strangeness**.

3) There are another three types of quark called **top**, **bottom** and **charm** (tut... physicists) that were predicted from the symmetry of the quark model. But luckily you don't have to know much about them...

The antiparticles of hadrons are made from **antiquarks**.

Quarks and Antiquarks have Opposite Properties

The **antiquarks** have **opposite properties** to the quarks — as you'd expect.

QUARKS

name	symbol	charge	baryon number	strangeness
up	u	$+\frac{2}{3}$	$+\frac{1}{3}$	0
down	d	$-\frac{1}{3}$	$+\frac{1}{3}$	0
strange	s	$-\frac{1}{3}$	$+\frac{1}{3}$	-1

ANTIQUARKS

name	symbol	charge	baryon number	strangeness
anti-up	$\bar{u}$	$-\frac{2}{3}$	$-\frac{1}{3}$	0
anti-down	$\bar{d}$	$+\frac{1}{3}$	$-\frac{1}{3}$	0
anti-strange	$\bar{s}$	$+\frac{1}{3}$	$-\frac{1}{3}$	$+1$

Baryons are Made from Three Quarks

Evidence for quarks came from **hitting protons** with **high energy electrons**.
The way the **electrons scattered** showed that there were **three concentrations of charge** (quarks) **inside** the proton.

Proton = **uud**

Total charge
$= 2/3 + 2/3 - 1/3 = 1$

Baryon number
$= 1/3 + 1/3 + 1/3 = 1$

Neutron = **udd**

Total charge
$= 2/3 - 1/3 - 1/3 = 0$

Baryon number
$= 1/3 + 1/3 + 1/3 = 1$

Antiprotons are $\bar{u}\bar{u}\bar{d}$ and antineutrons are $\bar{u}\bar{d}\bar{d}$ — so no surprises there then.

Mesons are a Quark and an Antiquark

Pions are just made from **up** and **down** quarks and their **antiquarks**.
Kaons have **strangeness** so you need to put in **s** quarks as well
(remember that the **s** quark has a strangeness of S = −1).

Physicists love patterns. Gaps in patterns like this predicted the existence of particles that were actually found later in experiments. Great stuff.

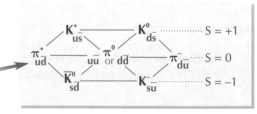

$$K^+_{u\bar{s}} \qquad K^0_{d\bar{s}} \quad\cdots\cdots S = +1$$
$$\pi^+_{u\bar{d}} \qquad \pi^0_{u\bar{u} \text{ or } d\bar{d}} \qquad \pi^-_{d\bar{u}} \cdots\cdots S = 0$$
$$\bar{K}^0_{s\bar{d}} \qquad K^-_{s\bar{u}} \quad\cdots\cdots S = -1$$

There's no Such Thing as a Free Quark

What if you **blasted** a **proton** with **enough energy** — could you **separate out** the quarks?
Nope. The energy just gets changed into more **quarks and antiquarks** — it's **pair production** again and you just make **mesons**.
This is called **quark confinement**.

Proton

Supply energy to separate the quarks

Quark-antiquark pair produced

Meson

Quarks

The **Weak Interaction** is something that Changes the **Quark Type**

In β⁻ decay a **neutron** is changed into a **proton** — in other words **udd** changes into **uud**.
It means turning a **d** quark into a **u** quark. Only the weak interaction can do this.

neutron → proton

Some unstable isotopes like **carbon-11** decay by β⁺ emission. In this case a **proton** changes to a **neutron**, so a **u** quark changes to a **d** quark and we get:

proton → neutron

Four Properties are **Conserved** in **Particle Reactions**

In **any** particle reaction, the **total charge** after the reaction must equal the total charge before the reaction. The same goes for **baryon number**.

The **only** way to change the **type** of quark is with the **weak interaction**, so in strong interactions there has to be the same number of strange quarks at the beginning as at the end.

The reaction $K^- + p \rightarrow n + \pi^0$ is fine for **charge** and **baryon number** but not for **strangeness** — so it won't happen. The negative kaon has an s quark in it.

The **three types** of lepton number have to be conserved **separately**.

1) For example, the reaction
   $\pi^- \rightarrow \mu^- + \overline{\nu}_\mu$ has $L_\mu = 0$ at the start and $L_\mu = 1 - 1 = 0$ at the end, so it's OK.

2) On the other hand, the reaction $\nu_\mu + \mu^- \rightarrow e^- + \nu_e$ can't happen.
   At the start $L_\mu = 2$ and $L_e = 0$ but at the end $L_\mu = 0$ and $L_e = 2$.

Sid had been conserving his strangeness for years...

Practice Questions

Q1 What is a quark?

Q2 Which type of particle is made from a quark and an antiquark?

Q3 Describe how a neutron is made up from quarks.

Q4 Explain why quarks are never observed on their own.

Q5 List four quantities that are conserved in particle reactions.

Exam Questions

Q1 State the combination of three quarks that make up a proton. [1 mark]

Q2 Give the quark composition of the π^- and explain how the charges of the quarks give rise to its charge. [2 marks]

Q3 Explain how the quark composition is changed in the β⁻ decay of the neutron. [2 marks]

Q4 Give two reasons why the reaction $p + p \rightarrow p + K^+$ does not happen. [2 marks]

A physical property called strangeness — how cool is that...

True, there's a lot of information here, but this page really does tie up a lot of the stuff on the last few pages. Learn as much as you can from this double page, then go back to page 52, and work back through to here. Don't expect to understand it all — but you will definitely find it much easier to learn when you can see how all the bits fit in together.

Binding Energy

Turn off the radio and close the door, 'cos you're going to need to concentrate hard on this stuff about binding energy...

The **Mass Defect** is **Equivalent** to the **Binding Energy**

1) The **mass** of a **nucleus** is **less than** the mass of its **constituent parts** — this is called the **mass defect** (see p. 51).

2) Einstein's equation, $E = mc^2$, says that mass and energy are **equivalent**.

3) So, as nucleons join together, the total mass **decreases** — this 'lost' mass is **converted** into energy and **released**.

4) The amount of **energy released** is **equivalent** to the **mass defect**.

5) If you **pulled** the nucleus completely **apart**, the **energy** you'd have to use to do it would be the **same** as the energy **released** when the nucleus formed.

> The energy needed to **separate** all of the nucleons in a nucleus is called the **binding energy** (measured in **MeV**), and it is **equivalent** to the **mass defect**.

Example Calculate the binding energy of the nucleus of a lithium atom, ^6_3Li, given that its mass defect is 0.0343 u.

1) Convert the mass defect into kg.

Mass defect = $0.0343 \times 1.66 \times 10^{-27} = 5.70 \times 10^{-29}$ kg

2) Use $E = mc^2$ to calculate the binding energy.

$E = 5.70 \times 10^{-29} \times (3 \times 10^8)^2 = 5.13 \times 10^{-12}$ J = 32 MeV

> Atomic mass is usually given in atomic mass units (u), where $1\ u = 1.66 \times 10^{-27}$ kg.

> $1\ \text{MeV} = 1.6 \times 10^{-13}$ J

6) The **binding energy per unit of mass defect** can be calculated (using the example above):

$$\frac{\text{binding energy}}{\text{mass defect}} = \frac{32\ \text{MeV}}{0.0343\ \text{u}} \approx 931\ \text{MeV u}^{-1}$$

7) This means that a mass defect of **1 u** is equivalent to about **931 MeV** of binding energy.

Captain Skip didn't believe in ghosts, marmalade and that things could be bound without rope.

The **Binding Energy Per Nucleon** is at a **Maximum** around **N = 50**

A useful way of **comparing** the binding energies of different nuclei is to look at the **binding energy per nucleon**.

> Binding energy per nucleon (in MeV) = $\dfrac{\text{Binding energy (B)}}{\text{Nucleon number (A)}}$

So, the binding energy per nucleon for ^6_3Li (in the example above) is $32 \div 6 = 5.3$ MeV.

1) A **graph** of **binding energy per nucleon** against **nucleon number**, for all elements, shows a **curve**.

2) **High** binding energy per nucleon means that **more energy** is needed to **remove** nucleons from the nucleus.

3) In other words the **most stable** nuclei occur around the **maximum point** on the graph — which is at **nucleon number 56** (i.e. **iron**, Fe).

4) **Combining small nuclei** is called nuclear **fusion** (see p. 61) — this **increases** the **binding energy per nucleon** dramatically, which means a lot of **energy is released** during nuclear fusion.

5) **Fission** is when **large nuclei** are **split in two** (see p. 60) — the **nucleon numbers** of the two **new nuclei** are **smaller** than the original nucleus, which means there is an **increase** in the binding energy per nucleon. So, energy is also **released** during nuclear fission (but not as much energy per nucleon as in nuclear fusion).

Binding Energy

The *Change* in *Binding Energy* Gives the *Energy Released...*

The **binding energy per nucleon graph** can be used to **estimate** the **energy released** from nuclear reactions.

Energy released in nuclear fusion

1) If ²H and ³H nuclei were **fused** together to form ⁴He (and a neutron), the **average increase** in binding energy per ⁴He nucleon would be about **5 MeV**.

2) There are **4 nucleons** in ⁴He, so we can **estimate** the **energy released** as $4 \times 5 = $ **20 MeV**.

Energy released in nuclear fission

1) If a ²³⁵U nucleus **splits** into ⁹²Rb and ¹⁴⁰Cs (plus a few neutrons) during nuclear **fission**, the **average increase** in **binding energy per nucleon** would be about 1.1 MeV.

2) There are **235 nucleons** in ²³⁵U to begin with, so we can **estimate** the energy **released** as $235 \times 1.1 \approx$ **260 MeV**.

Practice Questions

Q1 What is the binding energy of a nucleus?

Q2 How can we calculate the binding energy for a particular nucleus?

Q3 What is the binding energy per nucleon?

Q4 Which element has the highest value of binding energy per nucleon?

Q5 Do nuclear fusion or fission reactions release more energy per nucleon?

Exam Questions

Q1 The mass of a $^{14}_{6}\text{C}$ nucleus is 13.999948 u. The mass of a proton is 1.007276 u, and a neutron is 1.008665 u.

(a) Calculate the mass defect of a $^{14}_{6}\text{C}$ nucleus (given that 1 u = 1.66×10^{-27} kg). [3 marks]

(b) Use $E = mc^2$ to calculate the binding energy of the nucleus in MeV
(given that $c = 3 \times 10^8$ ms^{-1} and 1 MeV = 1.6×10^{-13} J). [2 marks]

Q2 The following equation represents a nuclear reaction that takes place in the Sun:

$$^{1}_{1}\text{p} + ^{1}_{1}\text{p} \rightarrow ^{2}_{1}\text{H} + ^{0}_{+1}\beta + \text{energy released}$$ where p is a proton and β is a positron (opposite of an electron)

(a) What type of nuclear reaction is this? [1 mark]

(b) Given that the binding energy per nucleon for a proton is 0 MeV and for a ²H nucleus it is approximately 0.86 MeV, estimate the energy released by this reaction. [2 marks]

A mass defect of 1 u is equivalent to a binding energy of 931 MeV...

Remember this useful little fact, and it'll save loads of time in the exam — because you won't have to fiddle around with converting atomic mass from u → kg and binding energy from J → MeV. What more could you possibly want...

Nuclear Fission and Fusion

What did the nuclear scientist have for his tea? Fission chips... hohoho.

Fission Means Splitting Up into Smaller Parts

1) **Large nuclei**, with at least 83 protons (e.g. uranium), are **unstable** and some can randomly **split** into two **smaller** nuclei — this is called **nuclear fission**.

2) This process is called **spontaneous** if it just happens **by itself**, or **induced** if we **encourage** it to happen.

Example

Fission can be induced by making a neutron enter a ^{235}U nucleus, causing it to become very unstable.

Only low energy neutrons can be captured in this way. A low energy neutron is called a **thermal neutron**.

3) **Energy is released** during nuclear fission because the new, smaller nuclei have a **higher binding energy per nucleon** (see p. 58).

4) The **larger** the nucleus, the more **unstable** it will be — so large nuclei are **more likely** to **spontaneously fission**.

5) This means that spontaneous fission **limits** the **number of nucleons** that a nucleus can contain — in other words, it **limits** the number of **possible elements**.

Controlled Nuclear Reactors Produce Useful Power

We can **harness** the **energy** released during nuclear **fission reactions** in a **nuclear reactor**, but it's important that these reactions are very **carefully controlled**.

1) Nuclear reactors use **rods of uranium** that are rich in ^{235}U as 'fuel' for fission reactions. (The rods also contain a lot of ^{238}U, but that doesn't undergo fission.)

2) These **fission** reactions produce more **neutrons** which then **induce** other nuclei to fission — this is called a **chain reaction**.

3) The **neutrons** will only cause a chain reaction if they are **slowed down**, which allows them to be **captured** by the uranium nuclei — these slowed down neutrons are called **thermal neutrons**.

4) ^{235}U **fuel rods** need to be placed in a **moderator** (for example, **water**) to **slow down** and/or absorb **neutrons**. You need to choose a moderator that will slow down some neutrons enough so they can cause **further fission**, keeping the reaction going at a steady rate. Choosing a moderator that absorbs **more neutrons the higher the temperature** will **decrease** the chance of **meltdown** if the reactor **overheats** — as it will naturally **slow down** the reaction.

5) You want the chain reaction to continue on its own at a **steady rate**, where **one** fission follows another. The amount of 'fuel' you need to do this is called the **critical mass** — any less than the critical mass (**sub-critical mass**) and the reaction will just peter out. Nuclear reactors use a **supercritical** mass of fuel (where several new fissions normally follow each fission) and **control the rate of fission** using **control rods**.

6) Control rods control the **chain reaction** by **limiting** the number of **neutrons** in the reactor. They **absorb neutrons** so that the **rate of fission** is controlled. **Control rods** are made up of a material that **absorbs neutrons** (e.g. boron), and they can be inserted by varying amounts to control the reaction rate.
In an **emergency**, the reactor will be **shut down** automatically by the **release of the control rods** into the reactor, which will stop the reaction as quickly as possible.

7) **Coolant** is sent around the reactor to **remove heat** produced in the fission — often the coolant is the **same water** that is being used in the reactor as a **moderator**. The **heat** from the reactor can then be used to make **steam** for powering **electricity-generating turbines**.

If the chain reaction in a nuclear reactor is **left to continue unchecked**, large amounts of **energy** are **released** in a very **short time**.

Many new fissions will follow each fission, causing a **runaway reaction** which could lead to an **explosion**. This is what happens in a **fission (atomic) bomb**.

Nuclear Fission and Fusion

Waste Products of Fission Must be Disposed of Carefully

1) The **waste products** of **nuclear fission** usually have a **larger proportion of neutrons** than stable nuclei of a similar atomic number — this makes them **unstable** and **radioactive**.

2) The products can be used for **practical applications** such as **tracers** in medical diagnosis (see p. 68).

3) However, they may be **highly radioactive** and so their **handling** and **disposal** needs **great care**.

4) When material is removed from the reactor, it is initially **very hot**, so is placed in **cooling ponds** until the **temperature falls** to a safe level.

5) The radioactive waste is then **stored** underground in **sealed containers** until its **activity has fallen** sufficiently.

Fusion Means Joining Nuclei Together

1) **Two light nuclei** can **combine** to create a larger nucleus — this is called **nuclear fusion**.

2) Nuclei can **only fuse** if they have enough energy to overcome the **electrostatic repulsive** force between them, and get close enough for the **strong interaction** to bind them.

3) Typically they need about **1 MeV** of kinetic energy — and that's **a lot of energy**.

Example

In the Sun, **hydrogen nuclei** fuse in a series of reactions to form **helium**.

$$^{2}_{1}H + {}^{1}_{1}H \rightarrow {}^{3}_{2}He + \text{energy}$$

Fusion Happens in the Core of Stars

1) The **energy** emitted by the **Sun** and other stars comes from nuclear **fusion** reactions.

2) Fusion can happen because the **temperature** in the **core of stars** is so **high** — the core of the Sun is about 10^7 K.

3) At these temperatures, **atoms don't exist** — the negatively charged electrons are **stripped away**, leaving **positively charged nuclei** and **free electrons**. The resulting mixture is called a **plasma**.

4) A lot of **energy** is released during nuclear fusion because the new, heavier nuclei have a **much higher binding energy per nucleon** (see p. 58). This helps to **maintain the temperature** for further fusion reactions to happen.

5) Experimental **fusion reactors** like JET (the Joint European Torus) are trying to **recreate** these conditions to generate **electricity** (without all the nasty waste you get from fission reactors). Unfortunately, the electricity generated at the moment is **less** than the amount needed to get the reactor up to temperature. But watch this space...

Practice Questions

Q1 What is spontaneous fission?

Q2 How can fission be induced in ^{235}U?

Q3 Why must the waste products of nuclear fission be disposed of very carefully?

Q4 Describe the conditions in the core of a star.

Exam Questions

Q1 Nuclear reactors use carefully controlled chain reactions to produce energy.
(a) Explain what is meant by the expression 'chain reaction' in terms of nuclear fission. [2 marks]
(b) Describe and explain one feature of a nuclear reactor whose role is to control the rate of fission. Include an example of a suitable material for the feature you have chosen. [3 marks]
(c) Explain what happens in a nuclear reactor during an emergency shut-down. [2 marks]

Q2 Discuss two advantages and two disadvantages of using nuclear fission to produce electricity. [4 marks]

If anyone asks, I've gone fission... that joke never gets old...

So, controlled nuclear fission reactions can provide a shedload of energy to generate electricity. There are pros and cons to using fission reactors. They produce huge amounts of energy without so much greenhouse gas, but they leave behind some very nasty radioactive waste... But then, you already knew that — now you need to learn all the grisly details.

X-Ray Imaging

X-ray imaging is one kind of non-invasive diagnostic technique — these techniques let doctors see what's going on (or going wrong) inside your body, without having to open you up and have a look.

X-rays are Produced by Bombarding Tungsten with High Energy Electrons

1) In an X-ray tube, **electrons** are emitted from a **heated filament** and **accelerated** through a high **potential difference** (the **tube voltage**) towards a **tungsten anode**.

2) When the **electrons** smash into the **tungsten anode**, they **decelerate** and some of their **kinetic energy** is converted into **electromagnetic energy**, as **X-ray photons**. The tungsten anode emits a **continuous spectrum** of **X-ray radiation**.

3)

X-rays are also produced when beam electrons **knock out** other electrons from the **inner shells** of the **tungsten atoms**.

Electrons in the atoms' **outer shells** move into the **vacancies** in the **lower energy levels**, and **release energy** in the form of **X-ray photons**.

4) Only about **1%** of the electrons' **kinetic energy** is converted into **X-rays**. The rest is converted into **heat**, so, to avoid overheating, the tungsten anode is **rotated** at about 3000 rpm. It's also **mounted** on **copper** — this **conducts** the heat away effectively.

Beam Intensity is Power per Unit Area

The **intensity** of the X-ray beam is the **power (energy per second) per unit area** passing through a surface (at right angles). There are two ways to increase the **intensity** of the X-ray beam:

1) Increase the **tube voltage**. This gives the electrons **more kinetic energy**. Higher energy electrons can **knock out** electrons from shells **deeper** within the tungsten atoms.

2) Increase the **current** supplied to the filament. This liberates **more electrons per second**, which then produce **more X-ray photons per second**.

Charlotte thought landing on her head would get top marks for beam intensity.

Radiographers try to Produce a Sharp Image and Minimise the Radiation Dose

Medical X-rays are a compromise between producing really sharp, clear images, whilst keeping the amount of radiation the patient is exposed to as low as possible. To do this, radiographers:

1) Put the **detection plate close** to and the **X-ray tube far** from the patient and make sure the patient **keeps still**.

2) Put a **lead grid** between the patient and film to **stop** scattered radiation '**fogging**' the film and **reducing contrast**.

3) Use an **intensifying screen** next to the film surface. This consists of crystals that **fluoresce** — they **absorb X-rays** and re-emit the energy as **visible light**, which helps to develop the photograph quickly. A shorter exposure time is needed, keeping the patient's radiation dose lower.

X-Ray Imaging

X-Rays are Attenuated when they Pass Through Matter

When X-rays pass through matter (e.g. a patient's body), they are **absorbed** and **scattered**.
The intensity (*I*) of the X-ray beam **decreases** (attenuates) **exponentially** with **distance from**
the **surface** (*x*), according to the material's attenuation coefficient (*μ*), as the equation shows.

$$I = I_0 e^{-\mu x}$$

1) **Half-value thickness**, $x_{\frac{1}{2}}$, is the thickness of material required to **reduce** the **intensity** to **half** its **original value**.

   This depends on the **attenuation coefficient**
   of the material, and is given by: $$x_{\frac{1}{2}} = \frac{\ln 2}{\mu}$$

2) The **mass attenuation coefficient**, μ_m, for a material of density ρ is given by: $$\mu_m = \frac{\mu}{\rho}$$

X-rays are Absorbed More by Bone than Soft Tissue

X-rays are **attenuated** by **absorption** and **scattering**. The **three** main **causes** of this are:

1) The **photoelectric effect** — a **photon** with around **30 keV** of energy is absorbed by an **electron**, which is **ejected** from its atom. The gap in the **electron shell** is filled by another **electron**, which emits a **photon**.

2) **Compton scattering** — a **photon** with around **0.5-5 MeV** of energy knocks an **electron** out of an **atom**, which causes the **photon** to **lose energy** and be **scattered**.

3) **Pair production** — a **high** (> 1.1 MeV) **energy** photon **decays** into an **electron** and a **positron**.

How much **energy is absorbed** by a **material** depends on its **atomic number** — so tissues containing atoms with **different atomic numbers** (e.g. **soft tissue** and **bone**) will **contrast** in the X-ray image.

If the tissues in the region of interest have similar attenuation coefficients then artificial **contrast media** can be used — e.g. **barium meal**. **Barium** has a **high atomic number**, so it shows up clearly in X-ray images and can be followed as it moves along the patient's digestive tract.

Fluoroscopy and CT Scans use X-rays

1) **Moving images** can be created by **X-ray fluoroscopy**, using a **fluorescent screen** and an **image intensifier**.

2) **Computerised axial tomography** (CT or CAT) scans produce an image of a **two-dimensional slice** through the body. An **X-ray beam rotates** around the body and is picked up by thousands of **detectors**. A computer works out how much attenuation has been caused by each part of the body and produces a very **high quality** image. However, the machines are **expensive**.

3) Both these techniques involve a **high radiation dose** for the patient.

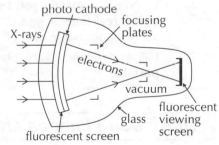

Practice Questions

Q1 Draw a diagram of an X-ray tube.

Q2 What measures can be taken to produce a high quality X-ray image while reducing the patient's radiation dose?

Exam Question

Q1 The half-value thickness for aluminium is 3 mm for 30 keV X-ray photons.

 (a) Explain what is meant by the term 'half-value thickness'. [1 mark]

 (b) What thickness of aluminium would reduce the intensity of a homogeneous beam of X-rays at 30 keV to 1% of its initial value? [4 marks]

I've got attenuation coefficient disorder — I get bored really easily...

X-ray images are just shadow pictures — bones absorb X-rays, stop them reaching the film and create a white 'shadow'.

Ultrasound Imaging

Ultrasound is a 'sound' with higher frequencies than we can hear.

Ultrasound has a Higher Frequency than Humans can Hear

1) Ultrasound waves are **longitudinal** waves with **higher frequencies** than humans can hear (>20 000 Hz).

2) For **medical** purposes, frequencies are usually from **1** to **15 MHz**.

3) When an ultrasound wave meets a **boundary** between two **different materials**, some of it is **reflected** and some of it passes through (undergoing **refraction** if the **angle of incidence** is **not 90°**).

4) The **reflected waves** are detected by the **ultrasound scanner** and are used to **generate an image**.

The Amount of Reflection depends on the Change in Acoustic Impedance

1) The **acoustic impedance**, *Z*, of a medium is defined as: $\boxed{Z = \rho c}$
   Z has units of $kgm^{-2}s^{-1}$.

2) Say an ultrasound wave travels through a material with an impedance Z_1. It hits the boundary between this material and another with an impedance Z_2. The incident wave has an intensity of I_i.

3) If the two materials have a **large difference** in **impedance**, then **most** of the energy is **reflected** (the intensity of the reflected wave I_r will be high). If the impedance of the two materials is the **same** then there is **no reflection**.

4) The **fraction** of wave **intensity** that is reflected is called the **intensity reflection coefficient**, α.

$$\alpha = \frac{I_r}{I_i} = \left(\frac{Z_2 - Z_1}{Z_2 + Z_1}\right)^2$$

You don't need to <u>learn</u> this equation. Just practise using it.

There are Advantages and Disadvantages to Ultrasound Imaging

ADVANTAGES:

1) There are **no** known **hazards** — in particular, **no** exposure to **ionising radiation**.

2) It's good for imaging **soft tissues**, since you can obtain **real-time** images — X-ray fluoroscopy can achieve this, but involves a huge dose of radiation.

3) Ultrasound devices are relatively **cheap** and **portable**.

DISADVANTAGES:

1) Ultrasound **doesn't penetrate bone** — so it **can't** be used to **detect fractures** or examine the **brain**.

2) Ultrasound **cannot** pass through **air spaces** in the body (due to the **mismatch** in **impedance**) — so it can't produce images from behind the lungs.

3) The **resolution** is **poor** (about 10 times worse than X-rays), so you **can't see** fine **detail**.

Ultrasound Images are Produced Using the Piezoelectric Effect

1) **Piezoelectric crystals** produce a **potential difference** when they are **deformed** (squashed or stretched) — the rearrangement in structure displaces the **centres of symmetry** of their electric **charges**.

2) When you **apply a p.d.** across a piezoelectric crystal, the crystal **deforms**. If the p.d. is **alternating**, then the crystal **vibrates** at the **same frequency**.

3) A piezoelectric crystal can act as a **receiver** of **ultrasound**, converting **sound waves** into **alternating voltages**, and also as a **transmitter**, converting **alternating voltages** into **sound waves**.

4) Ultrasound devices use **lead zirconate titanate** (**PZT**) crystals. The **thickness** of the crystal is **half the wavelength** of the ultrasound that it produces. Ultrasound of this frequency will make the crystal **resonate** (like air in an open pipe — see p.16) and produce a large signal.

5) The PZT crystal is **heavily damped**, to produce **short pulses** and **increase** the **resolution** of the device.

Ultrasound Imaging

You need a **Coupling Medium** between the **Transducer** and the **Body**

1) **Soft tissue** has a very different **acoustic impedance** from **air**, so almost all the ultrasound **energy** is **reflected** from the surface of the body if there is air between the **transducer** and the **body**.

2) To avoid this, you need a **coupling medium** between the transducer and the body — this **displaces** the **air** and has an impedance much closer to that of body tissue. **Coupling media** are an example of **impedance matching**.

3) The coupling medium is usually an **oil** or **gel** that is smeared onto the skin.

The **A-Scan** is a **Range Measuring** System

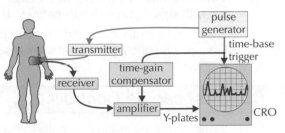

1) The **amplitude scan** (**A-Scan**) sends a short **pulse** of ultrasound into the body simultaneously with an **electron beam** sweeping across a cathode ray oscilloscope (**CRO**) screen.

2) The scanner receives **reflected** ultrasound pulses that appear as **vertical deflections** on the CRO screen.

3) **Weaker** pulses (that have travelled further in the body and **arrive later**) are **amplified** more to avoid the loss of valuable data — this process is called **time-gain compensation** (**TGC**).

4) The **horizontal positions** of the reflected pulses indicate the **time** the 'echo' took to return, and are used to work out **distances** between structures in the body (e.g. the **diameter** of a **baby's head** in the uterus).

5) A **stream** of pulses can produce a **steady image** on the screen due to **persistence of vision**, although modern CROs can store a digital image after just one exposure.

In a **B-Scan**, the **Brightness** Varies

1) In a **brightness scan** (**B-Scan**), the electron beam sweeps **down** the screen rather than across.

2) The amplitude of the reflected pulses is displayed as the **brightness** of the spot.

3) You can use a **linear array** of transducers to produce a **two-dimensional** image.

> **Ultrasound imaging** can also be used to measure the **speed of blood flow**.
> If the **ultrasound waves** reflect off something that is **moving** (e.g. **blood**), their **frequency** will be **shifted** according to the **Doppler effect** (see p.74). **How much** the reflected waves are **shifted** depends on **how fast** the blood is moving — so by **measuring the shift**, you can work out the **speed of blood flow**.

Practice Questions

Q1   What are the main advantages and disadvantages of imaging using ultrasound?

Q2   How are ultrasound waves produced and received in an ultrasound transducer?

Q3   Define acoustic impedance.

Exam Questions

Q1   (a) What fraction of intensity is reflected when ultrasound waves pass from air to soft tissue?
Use $Z_{air} = 0.430 \times 10^3 \text{ kgm}^{-2}\text{s}^{-1}$, $Z_{tissue} = 1630 \times 10^3 \text{ kgm}^{-2}\text{s}^{-1}$. [2 marks]

(b) Calculate the ratio between the intensity of the ultrasound that **enters** the body when a coupling gel is used
($Z_{gel} = 1500 \times 10^3 \text{ kgm}^{-2}\text{s}^{-1}$) and when none is used. Give your answer to the nearest power of ten. [4 marks]

Q2   (a) The acoustic impedance of a certain soft tissue is $1.63 \times 10^6 \text{ kgm}^{-2}\text{s}^{-1}$ and its density is $1.09 \times 10^3 \text{ kgm}^{-3}$.
Show that ultrasound travels with a velocity of 1.50 kms^{-1} in this medium. [2 marks]

(b) The time base on a CRO was set to be $50 \ \mu\text{scm}^{-1}$. Reflected pulses from either side of a fetal head are
2.4 cm apart on the screen. Calculate the diameter of the fetal head if the ultrasound travels at 1.5 kms^{-1}. [4 marks]

Ultrasound — Mancunian for 'très bien'

You can use ultrasound to make images in cases where X-rays would do too much damage — like to check up on the development of a baby in the womb. You have to know what you're looking for though, or it just looks like a blob.

Magnetic Resonance Imaging

Magnetic Resonance Imaging, or MRI to you and me, is yet another form of non-invasive diagnostic imaging — enjoy.

Magnetic Resonance can be used to Create Images

1) The patient lies in the centre of a huge **superconducting magnet** that produces a **uniform magnetic field**. The magnet needs to be **cooled** by **liquid helium** — this is partly why the scanner is so **expensive**.

2) Radio frequency **coils** are used to transmit **radio waves**, which **excite hydrogen nuclei** in the patient's body.

3) When the radio waves are switched off, the hydrogen nuclei relax and emit electromagnetic energy — this is the **MRI signal** (more details below). The radio frequency coils **receive the signal** and send it to a **computer**.

4) The computer **measures** various quantities of the MRI signal — amplitude, frequency, phase — and **analyses** them to generate an **image** of a **cross-section** through the body.

Contrast can be Controlled by Varying the Pulses of Radio Waves

1) Radio waves are applied in **pulses**. Each short pulse **excites** the hydrogen nuclei and then allows them to **relax** and emit a signal. The response of **different tissue types** can be enhanced by varying the **time between pulses**.

2) Tissues consisting of **large molecules** such as **fat** are best imaged using **rapidly repeated pulses**. This technique is used to image the internal **structure** of the body.

3) Allowing **more time** between pulses enhances the response of **watery** substances. This is used for **diseased** areas.

MRI has Advantages and Disadvantages

ADVANTAGES:

1) There are **no** known **side effects**.

2) An image can be made for any slice in any **orientation** of the body.

3) High quality images can be obtained for **soft tissue** such as the **brain**.

4) **Contrast** can be **weighted** in order to investigate different situations.

DISADVANTAGES:

1) The imaging of **bones** is very **poor**.

2) Some people suffer from **claustrophobia** in the scanner.

3) Scans can be **noisy** (due to the switching of the gradient magnets, see page 67) and take a **long time**.

4) MRI can't be used on people with **pacemakers** or some **metal implants** — the strong magnetic fields would be very harmful.

5) Scanners **cost millions** of pounds.

Atomic Nuclei can Behave like Magnets

1) **Protons** and **neutrons** possess a quantum property called **spin**, which makes them behave like **tiny magnets**.

2) If a nucleus has **even numbers** of **protons** and **neutrons** then the magnetic effects **cancel out**. A nucleus with an **odd number** of **protons** or **neutrons** has a **net spin** and is slightly **magnetic**.

3) The most important nucleus for **magnetic resonance imaging (MRI)** is **hydrogen**, which human bodies contain a lot of. A **hydrogen nucleus** has just **one proton**.

Protons Align themselves in a Magnetic Field

1) Normally, protons are orientated **randomly**, so their magnetic fields cancel out. When a strong **external magnetic field** is applied, as in an MRI scanner, the protons **align** themselves with the **magnetic field lines**.

2) Protons in **parallel alignment** point in the **same direction** as the external **magnetic field**. **Antiparallel alignment** means the protons point in the **opposite direction to the field**.

3) Protons align in these two directions in almost equal numbers (about 7 more per million are parallel). The **different alignments** correspond to **different energy levels**. The nuclei can **flip** between the two by **emitting** or **absorbing** a specific amount of **energy**.

$\Delta E \approx 2\ \mu eV$

Magnetic Resonance Imaging

Protons in a Magnetic Field Precess at the Larmor Frequency

1) Nuclei in a magnetic field don't just stay still — they **precess** (wobble) **around** the **magnetic field lines** (like a **spinning top** precessing around gravitational field lines).

2) They **don't** all precess **in phase** with each other.

3) All the protons **precess** at the **same frequency** — the **Larmor frequency, f**. The value of **f** depends on the **strength** of the **magnetic field, B_0**.

$$f = \frac{\gamma B_0}{2\pi}$$

γ = gyromagnetic ratio (in HzT^{-1}),
B_0 = magnetic flux density of the external field (in T).

precession — field line — spinning proton

4) For protons, $\frac{\gamma}{2\pi} = 42.57$ MHzT^{-1}.

> In an MRI scanner, the magnetic field, B_0 is about **1-2 teslas**, which puts **f** in the **radio** frequency range.
>
> There are also three **gradient magnets** — electromagnets which produce a very small field (superimposed on the main one) that gradually **varies** from place to place. The **Larmor frequency** depends on the **total magnetic flux density**, so **different frequencies** of radio wave can be used to target **different sites** within the body.

Radio Waves can Make Protons Resonate

1) Protons have a **natural frequency** of oscillation in a magnetic field which is **equal** to the **Larmor frequency, f**. **Radio waves** at this frequency can make protons **resonate**.

2) The protons **absorb energy** from the radio waves and **flip** from **parallel** to **antiparallel alignment**.

3) Radio waves at the Larmor frequency also make the protons precess **in phase** with each other, producing a **rotating magnetic field** at **right angles** to the external field.

4) When the **external radio waves stop**, the protons return to their **original states** and **emit electromagnetic energy** as they do so — this emitted energy is the MRI signal.

5) The time taken for the protons to return to their original state is called the **relaxation time**, and is about **one second**.

6) **Relaxation times** depend on what molecules surround the protons, so they **vary** for **different tissue types**.

parallel and antiparallel protons precessing in phase

B_0

this magnetic field rotates at the Larmor frequency

combined magnetic field of the protons

Practice Questions

Q1 Define the Larmor frequency and explain how radio waves at this frequency can cause resonance.

Q2 What is 'relaxation time' and how is this used to generate contrast within the images?

Q3 How do MRI scanners target protons from particular parts of the body?

Q4 Give two advantages of MRI compared to X-ray imaging.

Exam Questions

Q1 (a) Using a diagram, explain what is meant by the term 'precession'. [2 marks]

(b) What is the 'Larmor frequency'? Suggest a typical value for the Larmor frequency in an MRI scanner. [2 marks]

Q2 Outline how an MRI scanner is used to produce an image of a section of a patient's body. [5 marks]

Q3 Discuss the advantages and disadvantages of MRI scanning as a medical imaging technique. [6 marks]

Precession — protons on parade...

OK, so it hasn't been the easiest of pages. But at least now you know why people sit in vats of baked beans to raise money for their local hospital to buy an MRI scanner. Though perhaps you need A2 Psychology to understand the beans part.

Medical Uses of Nuclear Radiation

Radiation can be incredibly useful in medicine, but any use of radiation carries some risk.

Medical Tracers are Used to Diagnose the Function of Organs

Medical tracers are **radioactive substances** that are used to show tissue or **organ function**.
Other types of imaging, **e.g. X-rays**, only show the **structure** of organs — medical tracers show **structure and function**.
Medical tracers usually consist of a **radioactive isotope** — e.g. **technetium-99m** — bound to a **substance** that is **used**
by the **body** — e.g. **glucose** or **water**. The tracer is **injected** into or **swallowed** by the patient and then **moves** through
the **body** to the region of interest. **Where** the tracer goes depends on the **substance** the isotope is bound to — i.e. it
goes anywhere that the substance would **normally go**, and is used how that substance is **normally used**. The **radiation**
emitted is **recorded** (e.g. by a **gamma camera** or **PET scanner**, see below) and an **image** of inside the patient produced.

1) Tracers can show areas of damaged tissue in the heart by detecting areas of decreased blood flow.
This can reveal coronary artery disease and damaged or dead heart muscle caused by heart attacks.

2) They can identify active cancer tumours by showing metabolic activity in tissue. Cancer cells have
a much higher metabolism than healthy cells because they're growing fast, so take up more tracer.

3) Tracers can show blood flow and activity in the brain. This helps research and treat neurological
conditions like Parkinson's, Alzheimer's, epilepsy, depression, etc.

Technetium-99m is widely used in medical tracers because it emits γ-**radiation**, has a **half-life of 6 hours** (long
enough for data to be recorded, but short enough to limit the radiation to an acceptable level) and **decays** to a **much
more stable isotope**.

Gamma Cameras Detect Gamma Radiation

The γ-**rays** emitted by **radiotracers** injected into a patient's body are detected using a **gamma camera**.
Gamma cameras (like the one shown **below**) consist of **five** main parts:

1) **Lead shield** — **stops radiation** from **other sources** entering the camera.

2) **Lead collimator** — a **piece of lead** with thousands of **vertical holes**
in it — only γ-rays **parallel** to the holes can **pass through**.

3) **Sodium iodide crystal** — emits a **flash of light** (**scintillates**) whenever
a γ-**ray** hits it.

4) **Photomultiplier tubes** — **detect** the flashes of **light** from the crystal
and turn them into **pulses of electricity**.

5) **Electronic circuit** — **collects** the **signals** from the photomultiplier
tubes and sends them to a **computer** for processing into an **image**.

PET Scanning Involves Positron/Electron Annihilation

1) The patient is injected with a substance used by the
body, e.g. glucose, containing a **positron-emitting**
radiotracer with a **short half-life**, e.g. ^{13}N, ^{15}O, ^{18}F.

2) The patient is left for a time to allow the radiotracer
to **move through the body** to the organs.

3) **Positrons** emitted by the radioisotope collide with
electrons in the organs, causing them to **annihilate**,
emitting **high-energy gamma rays** in the process.

4) **Detectors** around the body record these **gamma
rays**, and a computer builds up a **map of the
radioactivity** in the body.

map of a 'slice' through
patient's head showing
concentration of radiotracer

5) The **distribution of radioactivity** matches up with **metabolic activity**. This is because **more** of the radioactive
glucose (or whatever) injected into the patient is taken up and **used** by cells that are **doing more work** (cells
with an **increased metabolism**, in other words).

Medical Uses of Nuclear Radiation

Ionising Radiation is Used When the Benefits Outweigh the Risks

X-rays, γ-rays, and α and β particles are all classed as **ionising radiation**. When they **interact** with matter they **ionise atoms** or **molecules** to form **ions** — usually by **removing an electron** — and this can **damage** cells.
Cell damage is bad news — it can cause:

1) **Cell mutations** and **cancerous tumours** by altering or damaging the cell's DNA.
2) **Cell sterility** by stopping the cell from reproducing.
3) **Cell death** — the cell is destroyed completely.

The **macroscopic effects** of ionising radiation (i.e. the large-scale effects) include **tumours**, **skin burns**, **sterility**, **radiation sickness**, **hair loss** and **death** — nice. The result is that radiation is only used when the **benefits** to the patient **outweigh the risks** — i.e. **radiation** doses are **limited** and only used when it's **absolutely necessary**.

Exposure, Absorbed Dose and Effective Dose

1) **Exposure** is defined as the **total charge produced** by ionising radiation **per unit mass of air**. The unit of exposure is the C kg^{-1}.

Air is used since its average atomic number is similar to that of body tissue.

2) The **absorbed dose** is more useful in medical physics because it is a measure of the **energy absorbed per unit mass**. The unit is the **gray** (**Gy**) where 1 Gy = 1 Jkg^{-1}.

3) The **effective dose**, H, takes into account the fact that the **amount of damage** to body tissue depends on the **type of ionising radiation**. The unit is the **sievert** (**Sv**) where 1 Sv = 1 Jkg^{-1}.

$$H = Q \times D$$
where H is the effective dose (Sv), Q is the quality factor, and D is the absorbed dose (Gy)

4) **Each type** of radiation is assigned a weighted **quality factor**, Q — the **greater** the **damage** produced by a type of radiation, the **higher** the quality factor. →

Radiation	Q
X-ray, β, γ	1
neutrons	5 - 20
α	20

Example Which absorbed dose would cause the greatest damage to a cell, 5 Gy of α or 10 Gy of β radiation?
To compare the potential damage to the cell you need to look at the effective dose of each type of radiation.

$$H_\alpha = 20 \times 5 = 100 \text{ Sv} \qquad H_\beta = 10 \times 1 = 10 \text{ Sv}$$

So **5 Gy of α** radiation would cause **more** cell damage than **10 Gy of β**.

Practice Questions

Q1 Why are medical tracers useful? Why are they dangerous?
Q2 What are the five main parts of a gamma camera?
Q3 Describe how an image is formed in PET scanning.
Q4 What's the difference between absorbed dose and effective dose?

Exam Questions

Q1 A doctor suspects that his patient has a cancerous tumour.
Describe a non-invasive technique that could be used to confirm the doctor's diagnosis. [3 marks]

Q2 A man of mass 70 kg accidentally swallows a source of α radiation (with a radiation quality factor of 20).
The source emits 3×10^{10} particles per second (constant over this time period) and the energy of each particle
is 8×10^{-13} J. The source is removed after 1000 seconds.
(a) Assuming that all the ionising energy is distributed uniformly around the man's body,
what is the absorbed dose that he receives? [2 marks]
(b) Calculate the effective dose. [1 mark]

The biological effects of a page on radiation — a sore head...

Hoo-bleeding-rah — at last, you've made it to the end of a proper beast of a section. But before you tootle off, just make sure you know the difference between absorbed dose and effective dose and can work each one out — there's bound to be a question on them in your exam. Oh, and don't forget to come back for the next section — it's a real good 'un.

The Solar System & Astronomical Distances

The Meaning of Life, Part 6: A2 Physics...

Our **Solar System** Contains the **Sun**, **Planets**, **Satellites**, **Asteroids** and **Comets**

1) The **Universe** is **everything** that exists — this includes plenty you can see, like **stars** and **galaxies**, and plenty that you can't see, like **microwave radiation** (see page 75).

2) **Galaxies**, like our very own **Milky Way galaxy**, are clusters of **stars** and **planets** that are held together by gravity.

3) Inside the Milky Way is our **Solar System**, which consists of the **Sun** and all of the objects that **orbit** it:

Asteroid belt

The planets (in order): **Mercury**, **Venus**, **Earth**, **Mars**, **Jupiter**, **Saturn**, **Uranus** and **Neptune** (as well as the asteroid belt) all have nearly **circular** orbits. We used to call Pluto a planet too, but it's been reclassified now.

Remember — planets, moons and comets don't emit light; they just reflect it.

4) The orbits of the **comets** we see are **highly elliptical**. Comets are "**dirty snowballs**" that we think usually orbit the Sun about **1000 times further away** than **Pluto** does (in the "Oort cloud"). Occasionally one gets **dislodged** and heads towards the Sun. It follows a new elliptical orbit, which can take **millions of years** to complete. Some comets (from closer in than the Oort cloud) follow a **smaller orbit** and they return to swing round the Sun more regularly. The most famous is **Halley's comet**, which orbits in **76 years**.

Distances and **Velocities** in the Solar System can be Measured using **Radar**

1) **Radio telescopes** can be used to send **short pulses** of **radio waves** towards a planet or asteroid (a rock flying about the Solar System), which **reflect** off the surface and bounce back.

2) The telescope picks up the reflected radio waves, and the **time taken** (**t**) for them to return is measured.

3) Since we know the **speed** of radio waves (**speed of light, c**) we can work out the **distance**, *d*, to the object using:

$$2d = ct$$

It's 2d, not just d, because the pulse travels twice the distance to the object — there and back again.

4) If **two** short pulses are sent a certain **time interval** apart, you can measure the **distance** an object has moved in that time. From this time and distance, you can calculate the **average speed** of the object **relative** to Earth. More accurate measurements can be made using Doppler shifts (see p. 74).

Distances in the Solar System are Often Measured in **Astronomical Units (AU)**

1) From **Copernicus** onwards, astronomers were able to work out the **distance** the **planets** are from the Sun **relative** to the Earth, using **astronomical units** (AU). But they could not work out the **actual distances**.

> One **astronomical unit** (AU) is defined as the **mean distance** between the **Earth** and the **Sun**.

2) The **size** of the AU wasn't known accurately until 1769 — when it was carefully **measured** during a **transit of Venus** (when Venus passed between the Earth and the Sun).

Another Measure of Distance is the **Light-Year (ly)**

1) All **electromagnetic waves** travel at the **speed of light**, *c*, in a vacuum ($c = 3.00 \times 10^8$ ms^{-1}).

> The **distance** that electromagnetic waves travel through a vacuum in **one year** is called a **light-year** (**ly**).

2) If we see the light from a star that is, say, **10 light-years away** then we are actually seeing it as it was **10 years ago**. The further away the object is, the further **back in time** we are actually seeing it.

3) **1 ly** is equivalent to about **63 000 AU**.

The Solar System & Astronomical Distances

The *Distance* to *Nearby Stars* can be Measured in *Parsecs*

1) Imagine you're in a **moving car**. You see that (stationary) objects in the **foreground** seem to be **moving faster** than objects in the **distance**. This **apparent change in position** is called **parallax**.

2) Parallax is measured in terms of the **angle of parallax**. The **greater** the **angle**, the **nearer** the object is to you.

3) The distance to **nearby stars** can be calculated by observing how they **move relative** to **very distant stars** when the Earth is in **different parts** of its **orbit**. This gives a **unit** of distance called a **parsec (pc)**.

A star is exactly **one parsec (pc)** away from Earth if the **angle of parallax**,

$$\theta = \textbf{1 arcsecond} = \left(\frac{1}{3600}\right)^{\circ}$$

Important *Sizes* and *Conversions*

You need to be able to state the length of a light-year and a parsec in metres. So here's a handy table to help you.

Unit of Distance	Light-year (ly)	Parsec (pc)	Astronomical Unit (AU)
Approximate Length in metres	9.46×10^{15}	3.09×10^{16}	1.50×10^{11}

You don't need to learn the length of an AU — it's just here for comparison.

When we look at the stars we're looking **back in time**, and we can only see as far back as the **beginning of the Universe**. So the **size** of the **observable Universe** is the **age** of the Universe multiplied by the **speed of light**.

Practice Questions

Q1 What are the principal contents of : a) the Universe, b) our Solar System?

Q2 What is meant by: a) an astronomical unit, b) a parsec, and c) a light-year?

Q3 How do we measure the distance to objects in the Solar System using radar?

Exam Questions

Q1 Outline the main differences between planets and comets. [5 marks]

Q2 (a) Give the definition of a *light-year*. [1 mark]

(b) Calculate the distance of a light-year in metres. [2 marks]

(c) Why is the size of the observable universe limited by the speed of light? [2 marks]

So — using a ruler's out of the question then...

Don't bother trying to get your head round these distances — they're just too big to imagine. Just learn the powers of ten and you'll be fine. Make sure you understand the definition of a parsec — it's a bit of a weird one.

Stellar Evolution

Stars go through several different stages in their lives — from clouds of dust and gas, to red giants to white dwarfs...

Stars Begin as Clouds of Dust and Gas

1) Stars are born in a **cloud** of **dust** and **gas**, most of which was left when previous stars blew themselves apart in **supernovae**. The denser clumps of the cloud **contract** (very slowly) under the force of **gravity**.

2) When these clumps get dense enough, the cloud fragments into regions called **protostars**, that continue to contract and **heat up**.

3) Eventually the **temperature** at the centre of a protostar reaches a **few million degrees**, and **hydrogen nuclei** start to **fuse** together to form helium (see page 61 for more on nuclear fusion).

4) This releases an **enormous** amount of **energy** and creates enough **pressure** (radiation pressure) to stop the **gravitational collapse**.

5) The star has now reached the **MAIN SEQUENCE** and will stay there, relatively **unchanged**, while it fuses hydrogen into helium.

Cloud of Dust and Gas

Protostar

Main Sequence Star

Main Sequence Stars become Red Giants when they Run Out of Fuel

1) Stars spend most of their lives as **main sequence** stars. The **pressure** produced from **hydrogen fusion** in their **core balances** the **gravitational force** trying to compress them. This stage is called **core hydrogen burning**.

2) When the **hydrogen** in the **core** runs out nuclear fusion **stops**, and with it the **outward pressure stops**. The core **contracts** and **heats up** under the **weight** of the star.

3) The material **surrounding** the core still has **plenty of hydrogen**. The **heat** from the contracting **core** raises the **temperature** of this material enough for the hydrogen to **fuse**. This is called **shell hydrogen burning**. (Very low-mass stars stop at this point. They use up their fuel and slowly fade away...)

4) The core continues to contract until, eventually, it gets **hot** enough and **dense** enough for **helium** to **fuse** into **carbon** and **oxygen**. This is called **core helium burning**. This releases a **huge** amount of energy, which **pushes** the **outer layers** of the star outwards. These outer layers **cool**, and the star becomes a **RED GIANT**.

5) When the **helium** runs out, the carbon-oxygen core **contracts again** and heats a **shell** around it so that helium can fuse in this region — **shell helium burning**.

Low Mass Stars (like the Sun) Eject their Shells, leaving behind a White Dwarf

1) In low-mass stars, the **carbon-oxygen core isn't hot enough** for any further **fusion** and so it continues to **contract** under its own **weight**. Once the core has shrunk to about **Earth-size**, **electrons** exert enough pressure (**electron degeneracy pressure**) to stop it collapsing any more (fret not — you don't have to know how).

2) The **helium shell** becomes more and more **unstable** as the core contracts. The star **pulsates** and **ejects** its outer layers into space as a **planetary nebula**, leaving behind the dense core.

3) The star is now a very **hot**, **dense solid** called a **WHITE DWARF**, which will simply **cool down** and **fade away**.

The Sun is a Main Sequence Star

The **Sun** might seem quite **special** to us on Earth — it's the reason we're all here after all. But really it's just like any other **low mass star** — it started off as a **cloud of dust and gas** and evolved to be the **main sequence star** we see today. Of course, this means it will most likely become a **red giant** and then finally fizzle out as a **white dwarf** — sob.

Cloud of Dust and Gas → Main Sequence Star → Red Giant → White Dwarf

Stellar Evolution

High Mass Stars have a Shorter Life and a more Exciting Death

The **mass** of a star will determine how it **evolves**. **Low to medium mass** stars (like the **Sun**) follow the sequence on the previous page. **High mass stars** (i.e. with around **8 times** the mass of the Sun, or more) follow the **sequence below**.

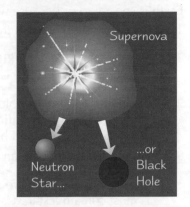

1) Stars with a **large mass** have a **lot of fuel**, but they use it up **more quickly** and don't spend so long as main sequence stars.

2) When they are **red giants** the **'core burning to shell burning'** process can continue beyond the fusion of helium, building up layers in an **onion-like structure** to become **SUPER RED GIANTS**.

3) For **really massive** stars, fusion can go all the way up to **iron**. Nuclear fusion **beyond iron** isn't **energetically favourable**, though, so once an iron core is formed then very quickly it's goodbye star.

4) The star explodes cataclysmically in a **SUPERNOVA**, leaving behind a **NEUTRON STAR** or (if the star was massive enough) a **BLACK HOLE**.

Massive Stars go out with a Bit of a Bang

1) When the core of a star runs out of fuel, it starts to **contract** — forming a white dwarf core.

2) If the star is **massive enough**, though, **electron degeneracy** can't stop the core contracting. This happens when the mass of the core is more than **1.4 times** the mass of the **Sun**.

3) The electrons get **squashed** onto the atomic **nuclei**, combining with protons to form **neutrons** and **neutrinos**.

4) The core suddenly collapses to become a **NEUTRON STAR**, which the outer layers then **fall** onto.

5) When the outer layers **hit** the surface of the **neutron star** they **rebound**, setting up huge **shockwaves**, ripping the star apart and causing a **supernova**. The light from a supernova can briefly outshine an **entire galaxy**!

Neutron Stars are Very Dense — But not as Dense as Black Holes

Neutron stars are incredibly **dense** (about 4×10^{17} kgm^{-3}).

They're **very small**, typically about 20 km across, and they can **rotate very fast** (up to 600 times a second).

They emit **radio waves** in two beams as they rotate. These beams sometimes sweep past the Earth and can be observed as **radio pulses** rather like the flashes of a lighthouse. These rotating neutron stars are called **PULSARS**.

If the **core** of a star is more than **3 times** the **Sun's mass**, it can't withstand the gravitational forces and collapses to form a **black hole**. The physics of black holes is mind-boggling, and luckily you don't need to know it.

Practice Questions

Q1 How are stars formed?

Q2 Outline the life cycle of the Sun, including its probable evolution and death.

Q3 What causes a star to evolve from the main sequence to become a red giant?

Q4 Describe a white dwarf and a neutron star. What are the main differences between them?

Exam Question

Q1 Outline the main differences between the evolution of high mass and low mass stars, starting from when they first become main sequence stars. [6 marks]

Live fast — die young...

The more massive a star, the more spectacular its life cycle. The most massive stars burn up the hydrogen in their core so quickly that they only live for a fraction of the Sun's lifetime — but when they go, they do it in style.

The Big Bang Model of the Universe

Everyone's heard of the Big Bang theory — well here's some evidence for it.

An **Infinite Universe** leads to **Olbers' Paradox**

It's easy to imagine that the Earth is at the **centre of the Universe**, or that there's something really **special** about it. **Earth** is special to us because we **live here** — but on a **universal scale**, it's just like any other lump of rock.

1) The **demotion** of **Earth** from anything special is taken to its logical conclusion with the **cosmological principle**...

> **COSMOLOGICAL PRINCIPLE**: on a **large scale** the Universe is **homogeneous** (every part is the same as every other part) and **isotropic** (everything looks the same in every direction) — so it doesn't have a **centre**.

2) Until the **1930s**, cosmologists believed that the Universe was **infinite** in both **space** and **time** (that is, it had always existed) and **static**. This seemed the **only way** it could be **stable** using **Newton's law** of gravitation. Even **Einstein modified** his theory of **general relativity** to make it consistent with the **Steady-State Universe**.

3) In the 1820s, though, an astronomer called **Olbers** noticed a **big problem** with this model of the Universe.

> If stars (or galaxies) are **spread randomly** throughout an **infinite** Universe then **every possible line of sight** must contain a **star**. Calculations show that this should make the **whole** night sky **uniformly bright**.

This problem is called **Olbers' paradox** and clearly there's a **contradiction** with an infinite and static Universe.

The **Doppler Effect** — the **Motion** of a Wave's **Source** Affects its **Wavelength**

1) Imagine an ambulance driving past you. As it moves **towards you** its siren sounds **higher-pitched**, but as it **moves away**, its **pitch** is **lower**. This change in **frequency** and **wavelength** is called the **Doppler shift**.

2) The frequency and the wavelength **change** because the waves **bunch together** in **front** of the source and **stretch out behind** it. The **amount** of stretching or bunching together depends on the **velocity** of the **source**.

3) This happens with light too — when a **light source** moves **away** from us, the wavelengths become **longer** and the frequencies become lower. This shifts the light towards the **red** end of the spectrum and is called **redshift**.

4) When a light source moves **towards** us, the **opposite** happens and the light undergoes **blueshift**.

5) The amount of redshift or blueshift is determined by the following formula:

$$z = \frac{\Delta\lambda}{\lambda} = \frac{v}{c} \text{ if } v \ll c$$

z is the redshift, $\Delta\lambda$ is the difference between the observed wavelength and the emitted wavelength, λ is the emitted wavelength, v is the velocity of the source in the direction of the observer and c is the speed of light. ($v \ll c$ means "v is much less than c".)

Hubble Realised that the **Universe** is **Expanding**

1) The **spectra** from **galaxies** (apart from a few very close ones) all show **redshift** — so they're all **moving away** from us. The amount of **redshift** gives the **recessional velocity** — how fast the galaxy is moving away.

2) Plotting **recessional velocity** against **distance** shows that they're **proportional** — i.e. the **speed** that **galaxies move away** from us depends on **how far** away they are.

3) This suggests that the Universe is **expanding**, and gives rise to **Hubble's law**:

$$v = H_0 d$$

where v = recessional velocity in **kms⁻¹**, d = distance in **Mpc** and H_0 = **Hubble's constant** in **kms⁻¹Mpc⁻¹**.

4) Since distance is very difficult to measure, astronomers disagree on the value of H_0. It's generally accepted that H_0 lies somewhere between 50 kms⁻¹Mpc⁻¹ and 100 kms⁻¹Mpc⁻¹.

5) The **SI unit** for H_0 is s⁻¹. To get H_0 in SI units, you need v in ms⁻¹ and d in m (1 Mpc = 3.09×10^{22} m).

The **Expanding Universe** gives rise to the **Hot Big Bang Model**

The Universe is **expanding** and **cooling down**. So further back in time it must have been **smaller** and **hotter**. If you trace time back **far enough**, you get a **Hot Big Bang**.

> **THE HOT BIG BANG THEORY (HBB):**
> the Universe started off **very hot** and **very dense** (perhaps as an **infinitely hot, infinitely dense** singularity) and has been **expanding** ever since.

If the Universe began at a specific point in time, i.e. in the HBB, then it has a finite age.

The Big Bang Model of the Universe

The *Age* and *Observable Size* of the *Universe* Depend on H_0

1) If the Universe has been **expanding** at the **same rate** for its whole life, the **age** of the Universe is: $\boxed{t = 1/H_0}$
This is only an estimate since the Universe probably hasn't always been expanding at the same rate.

2) Unfortunately, since no one knows the **exact value** of H_0 we can only guess the Universe's age.
If $H_0 = 75$ **kms^{-1}Mpc^{-1}**, then the age of the Universe $\approx 1/(2.4 \times 10^{-18}$ s$^{-1}) = 4.1 \times 10^{17}$ s = **13 billion years**.

3) The **absolute size** of the Universe is **unknown** but there is a limit on the size of the **observable Universe**.
This is simply a **sphere** (with the Earth at its centre) with a **radius** equal to the **maximum distance** that **light** can travel during its **age**. So if $H_0 = 75$ **kms^{-1}Mpc^{-1}** then this sphere will have a radius of **13 billion light years**.

4) This gives a very simple solution to **Olbers' paradox**. If the observable Universe is **finite**, then there is **absolutely no reason** why every line of sight should include a star. Actually, most of them don't.

Cosmic Microwave Background Radiation — *More Evidence for the HBB*

1) The Hot Big Bang model predicts that loads of **electromagnetic radiation** was produced in the **very early Universe**. This radiation should **still** be observed today (it hasn't had anywhere else to go).

2) Because the Universe has **expanded**, the wavelengths of this cosmic background radiation have been **stretched** and are now in the **microwave** region.

3) Cosmic microwave background radiation (CMBR) was picked up **accidentally** by Penzias and Wilson in the 1960s.

4) In the late 1980s a satellite called the **Cosmic Background Explorer** (**COBE**) was sent up to have a **detailed look** at the radiation. It found a **continuous spectrum** corresponding to a **temperature** of about **3 K**.

5) The radiation is largely **isotropic** and **homogeneous**, which confirms the cosmological principle (see page 64).

6) There are **very tiny fluctuations** in temperature, which were at the limit of COBE's detection. These are due to tiny energy-density variations in the early Universe, and are needed for the initial 'seeding' of galaxy formation.

7) The background radiation also shows a **Doppler shift**, indicating the Earth's motion through space. It turns out that the **Milky Way** is rushing towards an unknown mass (the **Great Attractor**) at over a **million miles an hour**.

Practice Questions

Q1   State Olbers' paradox. How does the Hot Big Bang model resolve it?

Q2   What is Hubble's law? How can it be used to find the age of the Universe?

Q3   What is the cosmic background radiation?

Exam Questions

Q1   (a) State Hubble's law, explaining the meanings of all the symbols.   [2 marks]

(b) What does Hubble's law suggest about the nature of the Universe?   [2 marks]

(c) Assume $H_0 = +50$ kms^{-1}Mpc^{-1} (1 Mpc = 3.09×10^{22} m).
  i) Calculate H_0 in SI units.   [2 marks]
  ii) Calculate an estimate of the age of the Universe, and hence the size of the observable Universe.   [3 marks]

Q2   (a) A certain object has a redshift of 0.37. Estimate the speed at which it is moving away from us.   [2 marks]

(b) Use Hubble's law to estimate the distance (in light years) that the object is from us.
    (Take $H_0 = 2.4 \times 10^{-18}$ s^{-1}, 1 ly = 9.5×10^{15} m.)   [2 marks]

Q3   Describe the main features of the cosmic background radiation and explain why its discovery
     was considered strong evidence for the Hot Big Bang model of the Universe.
     In your answer, you should make clear how your explanation links with the evidence.   [7 marks]

My Physics teacher was a Great Attractor — everyone fell for him...

The simple Big Bang model doesn't actually work — not quite, anyway. There are loads of little things that don't quite add up. Modern cosmologists are trying to improve the model using a period of very rapid expansion called inflation.

Evolution of the Universe

This page assumes the Standard Big Bang Model — so we can ignore newfangled theories like inflation (for now...)

Gravity Warps Space and Time

1) According to **general relativity** gravity works by changing the **shape** of space and time.

2) To reduce the brain-ache a bit, you can imagine the Universe as a **2-dimensional surface** that's warped in 3 dimensions. This is a handy way of getting an idea of what's going on, but **be careful**. Space-time actually has **4 dimensions** (x, y, z and time).

3) On a big scale, there are **three ways** that gravity can warp the Universe: the Universe can be **flat**, **open**, or **closed**.

4) This **curvature** of space-time determines the eventual **fate** of the Universe.

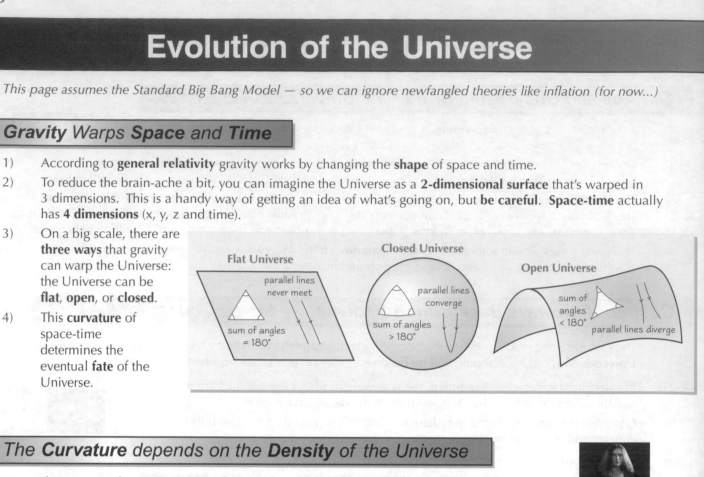

Flat Universe
parallel lines never meet
sum of angles = 180°

Closed Universe
parallel lines converge
sum of angles > 180°

Open Universe
sum of angles < 180°
parallel lines diverge

The Curvature depends on the Density of the Universe

1) The amount of **curvature** depends on the **average density** of the Universe, ρ_0.

2) The density required for the Universe to be **flat** is called the **critical density**, ρ_c.

> If $\rho_0 = \rho_c$ the Universe is **flat**, if $\rho_0 < \rho_c$ the Universe is **open** and if $\rho_0 > \rho_c$ it's **closed**.

With a bit of mathematical jiggery-pokery you can get an equation for the critical density of the Universe in terms of the Hubble constant:

$$\rho_0 = \frac{3H_0^2}{8\pi G}$$

The mists are clearing...

G is the gravitational constant — $6.67 \times 10^{-11} \, Nm^2kg^{-2}$.

3) The three possible types of **curvature** give three possible **fates** of the Universe:

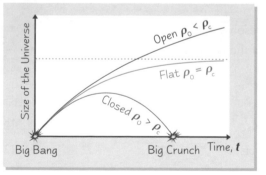

Size of the Universe

Open $\rho_0 < \rho_c$

Flat $\rho_0 = \rho_c$

Closed $\rho_0 > \rho_c$

Big Bang — Big Crunch — Time, t

In an **open** Universe, gravity (controlled by the density) is **too weak** to stop the expansion. The Universe will just keep **expanding for ever**.

In a **closed** Universe, gravity is **strong enough** to stop the expansion and start the Universe **contracting** again (ending up with a **Big Crunch**).

In a **flat** Universe, gravity is **just strong enough** to stop the expansion at $t = \infty$ (so the Universe expands for ever, but more and more slowly with time).

We Can't Calculate the Age of the Universe until we know its Density

1) A reasonable **estimate** of the **age** of the Universe is found from $t \approx 1/H_0$ (see page 74). But this formula assumes that the Universe had been expanding at the **same rate** for its whole lifetime.

2) In fact if you look at the **graph** of size against time, the **expansion rate** of the Universe is **slowing down**, even for the **open Universe**. So in the past the Universe was expanding **faster** than it is now.

3) That means we've **overestimated** the time it's taken for the Universe to get to the size it is now.

4) The **more dense** the Universe is, the **younger** it must be.

5) If you include all the "**dark matter**" and "**dark energy**" that's been detected **indirectly**, current **estimates** of the actual density of the Universe aren't very far off the **critical density**.

Evolution of the Universe

The Story So Far...

Before 10^{-4} seconds after the Big Bang, this is mainly guesswork. There are plenty of theories around, but not much experimental evidence to back them up. The general consensus at the moment goes something like this:

1) **Big Bang to 10^{-43} seconds**. Well, it's anybody's guess, really. At this sort of size and energy, even general relativity stops working properly. This is the "infinitely hot, infinitely small, infinitely dense" bit.

2) **10^{-43} seconds to 10^{-4} seconds**. At the start of this period, there's no distinction between different types of force — there's just one grand unified force. Then the Universe expands and cools, and the unified force splits into gravity, strong nuclear, weak nuclear and electromagnetic forces. Many cosmologists believe the Universe went through a rapid period of expansion called inflation at about 10^{-34} s.

   The Universe is a sea of quarks, antiquarks, leptons and photons. The quarks aren't bound up in particles like protons and neutrons, because there's too much energy around.

   At some point, matter-antimatter symmetry gets broken, so slightly more matter is made than antimatter. Nobody knows exactly how or when this happened, but most cosmologists like to put it as early as possible in the history of the Universe (before inflation, even).

Now we're onto more solid ground

3) **10^{-4} seconds**. This corresponds to a temperature of about 10^{12} K. The Universe is cool enough for quarks to join up to form particles like protons and neutrons. They can never exist separately again. Matter and antimatter annihilate each other, leaving a small excess of matter and huge numbers of photons (resulting in the cosmic background radiation that we observe today).

4) **About 100 seconds**. Temperature has cooled to 10^9 K. The Universe is similar to the interior of a star. Protons are cool enough to fuse to form helium nuclei.

5) **About 300 000 years**. Temperature has cooled to about 3000 K. The Universe is cool enough for electrons (that were produced in the first millisecond) to combine with helium and hydrogen nuclei to form atoms. The Universe becomes transparent since there are no free charges for the photons to interact with. This process is called recombination.

6) **About 14 billion years (now)**. Temperature has cooled to about 3 K. Slight density fluctuations in the Universe mean that, over time, clumps of matter have been condensed by gravity into galactic clusters, galaxies and individual stars.

Practice Questions

Q1 What are the three possible fates of the Universe?

Q2 Why does the calculated age of the Universe depend on its density?

Q3 What is recombination?

Exam Questions

Q1 (a) Some cosmologists believe the Universe to be flat. What evidence is there to suggest that this is the case? [2 marks]

   (b) Explain what is meant by a flat universe in terms of its geometry, and its evolution. [3 marks]

Q2 The upper limit on Hubble's constant is 100 kms^{-1}Mpc^{-1} (1 Mpc = 3.09×10^{22} m).

   (a) Work out the average density of the Universe if the Universe is flat and H_0 is 100 kms^{-1}Mpc^{-1}. [4 marks]

   (b) Given that the mass of a hydrogen atom is 1.7×10^{-27} kg, calculate the average number of hydrogen atoms in every m^3 of space if the entire mass of the Universe is hydrogen. [2 marks]

Q3 Starting from the production of matter and antimatter, describe the evolution of the Universe (including its structure) up to the present day.
   In your answer, you should use a clear, logical progression of ideas. [10 marks]

It's the end of the world as we know it...

Recently, astronomers have found evidence that the expansion rate is actually <u>accelerating</u> — because of something called dark energy. That means the simple shapes of the graphs on the last page might be a long way from the true picture...

Exponentials and Natural Logs

Mwah ha ha ha... you've hacked your way through the rest of the book and think you've finally got to the end of A2 Physics, but no, there's this tasty titbit of exam fun to go. You can get asked to look at and work out values from log graphs all over the shop, from astrophysics to electric field strength. And it's easy when you know how...

Many Relationships in Physics are **Exponential**

A fair few of the relationships you need to know about in A2 Physics are **exponential** — where the **rate of change** of a quantity is **proportional** to the **amount** of the quantity left. Here are just a few you should have met before (if they don't ring a bell, go have a quick read about them)...

Charge on a capacitor — the decay of charge on a capacitor is proportional to the amount of charge left on the capacitor: $Q = Q_o\, e^{(-t/RC)}$ (see p. 39)

Radioactive decay — the rate of decay is proportional to the **number of nuclei left** to decay in a sample: $N = N_o\, e^{(-\lambda t)}$ (see p. 49)

The **activity** of a radioactive sample behaves in the same way: $A = A_o\, e^{(-\lambda t)}$ (see p. 49)

You can **Plot** Exponential Relations Using the **Natural Log, ln**

1) Say you've got two variables, x and y, which are related to each other by the formula $y = ke^{-ax}$ (where k and a are constants).

2) The inverse of e is the natural logarithm, **ln**.

3) By definition, $\ln(e^x) = x$. So far so good... now you need some **log rules**:

$$\ln(ab) = \ln a + \ln b \qquad \ln\left(\frac{a}{b}\right) = \ln a - \ln b \qquad \ln a^b = b \ln a$$

When it came to logs, Geoff always took time to smell the flowers...

You don't need to learn these log rules — you're given them on your formula sheet.

4) So, if you take the natural log of the exponential function you get:

$\ln y = \ln(ke^{-ax}) = \ln k + \ln(e^{-ax}) \implies \boxed{\ln y = \ln k - ax}$

5) Then all you need to do is plot $(\ln y)$ against x, and Eric's your aunty:

You get a **straight-line** graph with $(\ln k)$ as the **y-intercept**, and $-a$ as the **gradient**.

You Might be Asked to find the **Gradient** of a Log Graph...

This log business isn't too bad when you get your head around which bit of the log graph means what. On the plus side, they won't ask you to plot a graph like this (yipee) — they'll just want you to find the **gradient** or the **y-intercept**.

Example — finding the radioactive half-life of material X

The graph shows the radioactive decay of substance X.
(a) Find the initial number of atoms, N_o, in the sample.

You know that the number of radioactive atoms in a sample, N, is related to the initial number of atoms by the equation $N = N_o e^{-\lambda t}$.

So, $(\ln N) = (\ln N_o) - \lambda t$ and $\ln N_o$ is the y-intercept of the graph = 9.2, $N_o = e^{9.2} \approx$ **9900 atoms**.

(b) Find the decay constant λ of substance X.

$-\lambda$ is the gradient of the graph, so: $\lambda = \dfrac{\Delta \ln N}{\Delta t} = \dfrac{9.2 - 7.8}{30 \times 60 \times 60} = \dfrac{1.4}{108\,000} = 1.3 \times 10^{-5}\ \text{s}^{-1}\,(2\text{s.f.})$

Log Graphs and Long Answer Questions

You can Plot *Any Power Law* as a *Log-Log Graph*

You can use logs to plot a straight-line graph of **any power law** — it doesn't have to be an exponential.
Take the relationship between the energy stored in a spring, **E**, and the spring's extension, **x**:

$$E = kx^n$$

Take the log (base 10) of both sides to get:

$$\boxed{\log E = \log k + n \log x}$$

So **log k** will be the **y-intercept** and **n** the gradient of the graph.

Example

The graph shows how the intensity of radiation from the Sun, **I**, varies with its distance, **d**.
I is related to **d** by the power law **I = kd^n**. Find **n**.

$$\log I = \log (kd^n) = \log k + \log d^n$$
$$= \log k + n \log d.$$

so **n** is the **gradient** of the graph.
Reading from the graph:

$$n = \frac{\Delta \log I}{\Delta \log d} = \frac{15.4 - 5.4}{5 - 10} = \frac{10}{-5} = -2$$

And that's the End of Logs... Now *Explain Yourself*...

In A2, they often give a couple of marks for 'the quality of written communication' when you're writing a slightly long answer (and not just pumping numbers into an equation).
You can pick up a couple of easy marks just by making sure that you do the things in the fetching blue box.

1) **Explain** your ideas or argument **clearly** as this is usually what you'll get a mark for. And make sure you **answer the question** being asked — it's dead easy to go off on a tangent. Like my mate Phil always says... have I ever told you about Phil? Well he...

2) Write in **whole sentences**.

3) Use **correct spelling**, **grammar** and **punctuation**.

4) Also check how many marks the question is worth.
If it's only a two-marker, they don't want you to spend half an hour writing an essay about it.

Example A large group of people walk across a footbridge. When the frequency of the group's footsteps is 1 Hz, the bridge noticeably oscillates and 'wobbles'.
Fully describe the phenomenon causing the bridge to wobble.
Suggest what engineers could do to solve this problem.
In your answer, you should make clear how your solution links with the theory. [6 marks]

Good Answer

The pedestrians provide a driving force on the bridge causing it to oscillate. At around 1 Hz, the driving frequency from the pedestrians is roughly equal to the natural frequency of the bridge, causing it to resonate. The amplitude of the bridge's oscillations when resonating at 1 Hz will be greater than at any other driving frequency. The oscillations at this frequency are large enough to be noticed by pedestrians.

Engineers could fix this problem by critically damping the bridge to stop any oscillations as quickly as possible.

They could also adjust the natural frequency of the bridge so that it was not so close to a known walking frequency of large groups of people.

Bad Answer

resonance
driving frequency of group = nat. freq.
damping

There's nothing wrong with the physics in the bad answer, but you'd miss out on some nice easy marks just for not bothering to link your thoughts together properly or put your answer into proper sentences.

Lumberjacks are great musicians — they have a natural logarithm...

Well, that's it folks. Crack open the chocolate bar of victory and know you've earnt it. Only the tiny detail of the actual exam to go... ahem. Make sure you know which bit means what on a log graph and you'll pick up some nice easy marks. Other than that, stay calm, be as clear as you can and good luck — I've got my fingers, toes and eyes crossed for you.

Answers

Unit 4: Section 1 — Newton's Laws and Momentum
Page 5 — Momentum and Impulse

1) a) total momentum before collision = total momentum after [1 mark]
   $(0.6 \times 5) + 0 = (0.6 \times -2.4) + 2v$
   $3 + 1.44 = 2v$ [1 mark for working] $\Rightarrow v = 2.22 \ ms^{-1}$ [1 mark]
   b) Kinetic energy before collision = $\frac{1}{2} \times 0.6 \times 5^2 + \frac{1}{2} \times 2 \times 0^2 = 7.5 \ J$
   Kinetic energy after the collision = $\frac{1}{2} \times 0.6 \times 2.4^2 + \frac{1}{2} \times 2 \times 2.22^2$
   $= 1.728 + 4.9284 = 6.6564 \ J$ [1 mark]
   The kinetic energy of the two balls is greater before the collision
   than after (i.e. it's not conserved) [1 mark], so the collision must
   be inelastic [1 mark].
2) momentum before = momentum after [1 mark]
   $(0.7 \times 0.3) + 0 = 1.1v$
   $0.21 = 1.1v$ [1 mark for working] $\Rightarrow v = 0.19 \ ms^{-1}$ [1 mark]

Page 7 — Newton's Laws of Motion

1) a) When the parachutist first jumps out of the plane, the only vertical
   force acting on her is due to gravity, so there is a resultant downward
   force [1 mark]. Newton's 2nd law states that the acceleration of a
   body is proportional to the resultant force, so she will accelerate
   downwards [1 mark].
   b) $F = ma = mg = 78 \times 9.81 = 765.18 \ N$ [1 mark]
   c) Newton's 1st law states that a force is needed to change the velocity
   of an object [1 mark] — the parachutist's velocity is not changing,
   so the resultant force acting on her must be zero [1 mark].
2) Force perpendicular to river flow = $500 - 100 = 400 \ N$ [1 mark]
   Force parallel to river flow = $300 \ N$

   Resultant force = $\sqrt{400^2 + 300^2} = 500 \ N$ [1 mark]

   $a = F/m$ [1 mark] $= 500/250 = 2 \ ms^{-2}$ [1 mark]

Unit 4: Section 2 — Circular Motion and Oscillations
Page 9 — Circular Motion

1) a) $\omega = \dfrac{\theta}{t}$ [1 mark] so $\omega = \dfrac{2\pi}{3.2 \times 10^7} = 2.0 \times 10^{-7} \ rad \ s^{-1}$ [1 mark]
   b) $v = r\omega$ [1 mark] $= 1.5 \times 10^{11} \times 2.0 \times 10^{-7} = 30 \ kms^{-1}$ [1 mark]
   c) $F = m\omega^2 r$ [1 mark] $= 6.0 \times 10^{24} \times (2.0 \times 10^{-7})^2 \times 1.5 \times 10^{11}$
   $= 3.6 \times 10^{22} \ N$ [1 mark]
   The answers to b) and c) use the rounded value of ω calculated in
   part a) — if you didn't round, your answers will be slightly different.
   d) The gravitational force between the Sun and the Earth [1 mark]
2) a) Gravity pulling down on the water at the top of the swing gives a
   centripetal acceleration of $9.81 \ ms^{-2}$ [1 mark]. If the circular motion
   of the water needs a centripetal acceleration of less than $9.81 \ ms^{-2}$,
   gravity will pull it in too tight a circle. The water will fall out of the
   bucket.

   Since $a = \omega^2 r$, $\omega^2 = \dfrac{a}{r} = \dfrac{9.81}{1}$, so $\omega = 3.1 \ rad \ s^{-1}$ [1 mark]

   $\omega = 2\pi f$, so $f = \dfrac{\omega}{2\pi} = 0.5 \ rev \ s^{-1}$ [1 mark]
   b) Centripetal force = $m\omega^2 r = 10 \times 5^2 \times 1 = 250 \ N$ [1 mark].
   This force is provided by both the tension in the rope, T, and gravity:
   $T + (10 \times 9.81) = 250$. So $T = 250 - (10 \times 9.81) = 152 \ N$ [1 mark].

Page 11 — Gravitational Fields

1) $g = \dfrac{GM}{r^2} \Rightarrow M = \dfrac{gr^2}{G} = \dfrac{9.81 \times (6400 \times 1000)^2}{6.67 \times 10^{-11}}$ [1 mark]
   $= 6.02 \times 10^{24} \ kg$ [1 mark]

2) a) $g = \dfrac{GM}{r^2} = \dfrac{6.67 \times 10^{-11} \times 7.35 \times 10^{22}}{(1740 \times 1000)^2} = 1.62 \ Nkg^{-1}$ [1 mark]

   b) $F = -\dfrac{GMm}{r^2} = \dfrac{6.67 \times 10^{-11} \times 7.35 \times 10^{22} \times 25}{(1740 \times 1000 + 10)^2}$ [1 mark]

   $= 40.48 \ N$ [1 mark]

Page 13 — Motion of Masses in Gravitational Fields

1) a) $T = \sqrt{\dfrac{4\pi^2 r^3}{GM}} = \sqrt{\dfrac{4\pi^2 \times [(6400 + 200) \times 1000]^3}{6.67 \times 10^{-11} \times 5.98 \times 10^{24}}}$ [1 mark]
   $= 5334 \ seconds \ OR \ 1.48 \ hours$ [1 mark]

   b) $v = \sqrt{\dfrac{GM}{r}} = \sqrt{\dfrac{6.67 \times 10^{-11} \times 5.98 \times 10^{24}}{(6400 + 200) \times 1000}}$
   $= 7774 \ ms^{-1} \approx 7.77 \ kms^{-1}$ [1 mark]
2) Period = 24 hours = $24 \times 60 \times 60 = 86 \ 400 \ s$ [1 mark]

   $T = \sqrt{\dfrac{4\pi^2 r^3}{GM}} \Rightarrow r = \sqrt[3]{\dfrac{T^2 GM}{4\pi^2}} = \sqrt[3]{\dfrac{86400^2 \times 6.67 \times 10^{-11} \times 5.98 \times 10^{24}}{4\pi^2}}$
   $r = 4.23 \times 10^7 \ m = 4.23 \times 10^4 \ km$ [1 mark]
   Height above Earth = $4.23 \times 10^4 - 6.4 \times 10^3 = 35 \ 900 \ km$ [1 mark]
3) Over 50 000 years, the Sun will have only lost a tiny fraction of its
   mass (9.5×10^{21} kg overall) [1 mark], which will not have caused any
   significant change in the Earth's orbit [1 mark].

Page 15 — Simple Harmonic Motion

1) a) Simple harmonic motion is an oscillation in which an object always
   accelerates towards a fixed point [1 mark] with an acceleration
   directly proportional to its displacement from that point [1 mark].
   [The SHM equation would get you the marks if you defined all the
   variables.]
   b) The acceleration of a falling bouncy ball is due to gravity.
   This acceleration is constant, so the motion is not SHM. [1 mark].
2) a) Maximum velocity = $(2\pi f)A = 2\pi \times 1.5 \times 0.05 = 0.47 \ ms^{-1}$ [1 mark].
   b) Stopclock started when object released, so $x = A\cos(2\pi ft)$ [1 mark].
   $x = 0.05 \times \cos(2\pi \times 1.5 \times 0.1) = 0.05 \times \cos(0.94) = 0.029 \ m$
   [1 mark].
   c) $x = A\cos(2\pi ft) \Rightarrow 0.01 = 0.05 \times \cos(2\pi \times 1.5t)$.
   So $0.2 = \cos(3\pi t) \Rightarrow \cos^{-1}(0.2) = 3\pi t$. $3\pi t = 1.37 \Rightarrow t = 0.15 \ s$.
   [1 mark for working, 1 mark for correct answer]
   Don't forget to put your calculator in radian mode when you're solving
   questions on circular motion — it's an easy mistake to make.

Page 17 — Free and Forced Vibrations

1) a) When a system is forced to vibrate at a frequency that's close to, or
   the same as its natural frequency [1 mark] and oscillates with a much
   larger than usual amplitude [1 mark].
   b) See graph below. [1 mark] for showing a peak at the natural
   frequency, [1 mark] for a sharp peak.

   c) See graph. [1 mark] for a smaller peak at the natural frequency
   [the peak will actually be slightly to the left of the natural frequency
   due to the damping, but you'll get the mark if the peak is at the same
   frequency in the diagram].
2) a) A system is critically damped if it returns to rest in the shortest time
   possible [1 mark] when it's displaced from equilibrium and released.
   b) e.g. suspension in a car [1 mark].

Answers

Unit 4: Section 3 — Thermal Physics
Page 19 — Solids, Liquids and Gases

1) Electrical energy supplied:
$\Delta E = VI\Delta t = 12 \times 7.5 \times 180 = 16200$ J *[1 mark]*
The temperature rise is $12.7 - 4.5 = 8.2$ °C

Specific heat capacity: $c = \dfrac{\Delta E}{m\Delta\theta}$ *[1 mark]*

$= \dfrac{16200}{2 \times 8.2} = 988$ J kg^{-1}°C^{-1} *[1 mark]*

You need the right unit for the third mark — J kg^{-1} K^{-1} would be right too.

2) a) A molecule's energy is the sum of its potential and kinetic energy *[1 mark]*. The water is at 373 K so the molecules have the same kinetic energy *[1 mark]* This means that one must have more potential energy than the other — i.e. one is liquid and the other is gas *[1 mark]*.

b) Total amount of energy needed to boil all the water:
$\Delta E = ml = 2.26 \times 10^6 \times 0.5 = 1.13 \times 10^6$ J *[1 mark]*
3 kW means you get 3000 J in a second, so
time in seconds $= 1.13 \times 10^6 / 3000$ *[1 mark]* $= 377$ s *[1 mark]*

Page 21 — Ideal Gases

1) a) i) Number of moles $= \dfrac{\text{mass of gas}}{\text{molar mass}} = \dfrac{0.014}{0.028} = 0.5$ *[1 mark]*

ii) Number of molecules = number of moles × Avogadro's constant
$= 0.5 \times 6.02 \times 10^{23} = 3.01 \times 10^{23}$ *[1 mark]*

b) $pV = nRT$, so $p = \dfrac{nRT}{V}$ *[1 mark]*

$p = \dfrac{0.5 \times 8.31 \times 300}{0.01} = 125\,000$ Pa *[1 mark]*

c) The pressure would also halve *[1 mark]* (because it is proportional to the number of molecules — $pV = NkT$).

2) $\dfrac{pV}{T} = $ constant

At ground level, $\dfrac{pV}{T} = \dfrac{1 \times 10^5 \times 10}{293} = 3410$ JK^{-1} *[1 mark]*

Higher up, pV/T will equal this same constant. *[1 mark]*
So higher up, $p = \dfrac{\text{constant} \times T}{V} = \dfrac{3410 \times 260}{25}$

$p = 35\,500$ Pa *[1 mark]*

Page 23 — The Pressure of an Ideal Gas

1) a) For example, put some smoke into a glass cell and shine a beam of light onto it *[1 mark]*. Use a microscope to view the smoke particles *[1 mark]*.

b) In Brownian motion, particles continually change direction so must be acted on by an external force *[1 mark]*. The nature of this force is uneven and random, which is consistent with a force caused by collisions between randomly moving particles *[1 mark]*.

c) The random movement of the particles causes them to collide with the container and exert an outward force *[1 mark]*.

Page 25 — Internal Energy and Temperature

1) a) 6.02×10^{23} molecules *[1 mark]*

b) $E = \dfrac{3}{2}kT$ *[1 mark]* $= [3 \times (1.38 \times 10^{-23}) \times 300] \div 2$

$= 6.21 \times 10^{-21}$ J *[1 mark]*

b) The nitrogen molecules are constantly colliding and transferring energy between themselves, so have different energies *[1 mark]*.

2) i) The average kinetic energy would halve because it is proportional to the absolute temperature *[1 mark]*.

ii) Internal energy is the sum of the kinetic energy of the particles so this would also halve *[1 mark]*.

iii) The mass of a molecule would not change because it is a physical property of the molecule and not dependent on temperature *[1 mark]*.

iv) Pressure is proportional to temperature, so the pressure would halve *[1 mark]*.

Unit 5: Section 1 — Electric and Magnetic Fields
Page 27 — Electric Fields

1)

+Q   -Q

Recognisable pattern around the charges (not just in between) *[1 mark]*, lines equally spaced around the charges and joined to the charges, and general symmetry of the diagram *[1 mark]*, arrows along field lines between the charges with arrows pointing away from the positive and towards the negative charge *[1 mark]*.

2) $E = \dfrac{Q}{4\pi\varepsilon_0 r^2}$

$= \dfrac{1.6\times10^{-19}}{4\pi \times 8.85\times10^{-12} \times (1.75\times10^{-10})^2}$

$= 4.698\times10^{10}$ *[1 mark]* Vm^{-1} or NC^{-1} *[1 mark]*

3) a) $E = V/d = 1500/(4.5 \times 10^{-3}) = 3.3 \times 10^5$ *[1 mark]* Vm^{-1} *[1 mark]*
The field is perpendicular to the plates. *[1 mark]*

b) $d = 2 \times (4.5 \times 10^{-3}) = 9.0 \times 10^{-3}$ m *[1 mark]*
$E = V/d \Rightarrow V = Ed = [1500/(4.5 \times 10^{-3})] \times 9 \times 10^{-3} = 3000$ V *[1 mark]*

Page 29 — Magnetic Fields

1) a) $F = BIl = 2 \times 10^{-5} \times 3 \times 0.04$ *[1 mark]* $= 2.4 \times 10^{-6}$ N *[1 mark]*

b) $F = BIl\sin\theta = 2.4 \times 10^{-6} \times \sin 30° = 2.4 \times 10^{-6} \times 0.5$ *[1 mark]*
$= 1.2 \times 10^{-6}$ N *[1 mark]*

Page 31 — Charged Particles in Magnetic Fields

1) a) $F = Bqv = 0.77 \times 1.6 \times 10^{-19} \times 5 \times 10^6$ *[1 mark]*
$= 6.16 \times 10^{-13}$ N *[1 mark]*

b) The force acting on the electron is always at right angles to its velocity and the speed of the electron is constant. This is the condition for circular motion. *[1 mark]*

2) Electromagnetic force = centripetal force *[1 mark]*
so, $Bqv = mv^2 / r$ *[1 mark]*

so, $r = \dfrac{mv}{Bq} = \dfrac{9.11\times10^{-31} \times 2.3\times10^7}{0.6\times10^{-3} \times 1.6\times10^{-19}} = 0.218$ m *[1 mark]*

3) $r = \dfrac{mv}{Bq}$ *[1 mark]*, which rearranges to give $B = \dfrac{mv}{rq}$.

v, r and q are all constant, so $\dfrac{B}{m} = $ constant *[1 mark]*
Find the constant when $B = 0.20$ T, $m = 35$: $0.20 \div 35 = 5.7 \times 10^{-3}$.
Now use this value to find B when $m = 37$:
$B = 37 \times 5.7 \times 10^{-3} = 0.21$ T *[1 mark]*

Page 33 — Electromagnetic Induction

1) a) $\phi = BA$ *[1 mark]* $= 2 \times 10^{-3} \times 0.23 = 4.6 \times 10^{-4}$ Wb *[1 mark]*

b) $\Phi = BAN$ *[1 mark]* $= 2 \times 10^{-3} \times 0.23 \times 150 = 0.069$ Wb *[1 mark]*

c) $V = \dfrac{\Delta\Phi}{\Delta t} = \dfrac{(B_{start} - B_{end})AN}{\Delta t}$

$= \dfrac{(2\times10^{-3} - 1.5\times10^{-3})(0.23\times150)}{2.5} = 6.9\times10^{-3}$ V

[3 marks available, one for each stage of the workings]

2) a) $\Phi = BAN$ *[1 mark]*
$= 0.9 \times 0.01 \times 500 = 4.5$ Wb *[1 mark]*

b) Find the flux linkage after the movement:
$\Phi = N\phi = NBA \cos\theta$ *[1 mark]*
$= 500 \times 0.9 \times 0.01 \times \cos(90) = 0$ Wb *[1 mark]*

$V = \dfrac{\Delta\Phi}{\Delta t}$ *[1 mark]*

$= \dfrac{4.5 - 0}{0.5} = 9$ V *[1 mark]*

82

Answers

Page 35 — Electromagnetic Induction

1) a) $V = Blv$ [1 mark] $= 60 \times 10^{-6} \times 30 \times 100 = 0.18$ V   [1 mark]

   b)

   [1 mark]

2) a) $\frac{V_p}{V_s} = \frac{N_p}{N_s}$ [1 mark] so, $N_s = \frac{45 \times 150}{9} = 750$ turns [1 mark]

   b) $\frac{V_s}{V_p} = \frac{N_s}{N_p}$ [1 mark] so, $V_s = \frac{V_p N_s}{N_p} = \frac{9 \times 90}{150} = 5.4$ V [1 mark]

   c) A transformer that increases the voltage [1 mark].

Unit 5: Section 2 — Capacitors and Exponential Decay

Page 37 — Capacitors

1) a) Capacitors are used to control a camera's flash by providing a short pulse of high current. [1 mark]

   b) Capacitors are suitable for this because they can deliver a short pulse of high current [1 mark], which results in a brief flash of bright light when needed [1 mark].

2) Capacitance $= \frac{Q}{V} = $ gradient of line $= \frac{660\ \mu C}{3\ V} = 220\ \mu F$.

   [1 mark for 'gradient', 1 mark for correct answer.]
   Charge stored $= Q = $ area $= 15 \times 10^{-6} \times 66 = 990\ \mu C$.
   [1 mark for 'area', 1 mark for correct answer.]

3) a) $W = \frac{1}{2}CV^2$ [1 mark] $= \frac{1}{2} \times 0.5 \times 12^2 = 36$ J [1 mark]

   b) $Q = CV$ [1 mark] $= 0.5 \times 12 = 6$ C [1 mark]

4) The voltage across all the components in a parallel circuit is the same as the source voltage, whereas in a series circuit the source voltage is shared between the components [1 mark]. This means that the two capacitors in parallel will each have a higher voltage across them than the two in series [1 mark]. Charge stored is proportional to voltage, so the capacitors in parallel will store more charge than those in series [1 mark]. [1 mark for a clear sequence of ideas.]

Page 39 — Charging and Discharging

1) a) The charge falls to 37% after CR seconds [1 mark], so $t = 1000 \times 2.5 \times 10^{-4} = 0.25$ seconds [1 mark]

   b) $Q = Q_0 e^{-\frac{t}{CR}}$ [1 mark], so after 0.7 seconds:

   $Q = Q_0 e^{-\frac{0.7}{0.25}} = Q_0 \times 0.06$ [1 mark]. There is 6% of the initial charge left on the capacitor after 0.7 seconds [1 mark].

   c) i) The total charge stored will double [1 mark].
      ii) None [1 mark].
      iii) None [1 mark].

Unit 5: Section 3 — Nuclear Physics

Page 41 — Scattering to Determine Structure

1) a) The nuclear model states that an atom consists of a central mass with a positive charge (the nucleus) [1 mark], surrounded by orbiting negative electrons [1 mark]. The nucleus makes up a tiny proportion of the volume of an atom, but most of its mass [1 mark].

   b) For alpha particles to pass straight through the foil, there must be a relatively large amount of empty space in an atom [1 mark]. For the alpha particles to be deflected at such large angles, the atom must contain a region of concentrated mass, greater than that of an alpha particle — the nucleus [1 mark]. This region must have the same charge as an alpha particle (positive) in order to deflect the particles [1 mark].

2) 8 protons, 8 electrons and 8 neutrons [2 marks for all correct, 1 mark for two correct]

Page 43 — Nuclear Radius and Density

1) Isotopes are atoms with the same number of protons, but different numbers of neutrons. / Isotopes are atoms with the same proton numbers, but different nucleon numbers [1 mark]. Two isotopes will have the same chemical properties as this depends on the number of protons [1 mark], but may have different nuclear stabilities [1 mark].

2) Volume $= \frac{4}{3}\pi r^3 = \frac{4}{3}\pi \left(8.53 \times 10^{-15}\right)^3 = 2.6 \times 10^{-42}$ m^3 [1 mark]

   So density $(\rho) = \frac{m}{V} = \frac{3.75 \times 10^{-25}}{2.6 \times 10^{-42}} = 1.44 \times 10^{17}$ kg m^{-3} [1 mark]

3) The density of a gold nucleus is much larger than the density of a gold atom [1 mark]. This implies that the majority of a gold atom's mass is contained in the nucleus [1 mark].
   The nucleus is small compared to the size of the atom [1 mark].
   There must be a lot of nearly empty space inside each atom [1 mark].

Page 45 — The Strong Nuclear Force

1) a) $F = \frac{1}{4\pi\varepsilon_o}\frac{Q_1 Q_2}{r^2} = \frac{1}{4\pi\left(8.85 \times 10^{-12}\right)}\frac{\left(1.6 \times 10^{-19}\right)\left(1.6 \times 10^{-19}\right)}{\left(9 \times 10^{-15}\right)^2} = 2.8$ N

   [1 mark for working, 1 mark for correct answer]

   b) The electrostatic force will increase [1 mark].

   c) There is no electrostatic force between a proton and a neutron [1 mark] because a neutron has no charge [1 mark].

2) a) The strong interaction must be repulsive at very small nucleon separations to prevent the nucleus being crushed to a point [1 mark].

   b) Beyond 10 fm, the strong interaction is smaller than the electrostatic force [1 mark]. This means the protons in the nucleus would be forced apart. So a nucleus bigger than this would be unstable. [1 mark]

Page 47 — Radioactive Emissions

1) Place different materials between the source and detector and measure the amount of radiation getting through [1 mark]:

   Skin or paper stops ALPHA | Few mm aluminium stops BETA | Many cm lead stops GAMMA

   [1 mark for each material stopping correct radiation]

2) a) Radioactive isotopes in smoke alarms ionise the air between two electrodes [1 mark], which allows current to flow [1 mark]. If there's a fire, smoke absorbs the radiation, the current stops and the alarm sounds [1 mark].

   b) Smoke alarms use sources of alpha radiation [1 mark]. Alpha radiation is sufficiently ionising to allow a current to flow between the electrodes [1 mark], but can only travel short distances so won't cause a hazard to people [1 mark].

Answers

Page 49 — Exponential Law of Decay

1) Any one of: You can't say which atom/nucleus in a sample will be the next one to decay. / You can only estimate the fraction of nuclei that will decay or the probability an atom/nucleus will decay in a given time. / You cannot say exactly how many atoms will decay in a given time. [1 mark]

2)a) Activity, A = measured activity – background activity
= 750 – 50 = 700 Bq [1 mark]
$A = \lambda N \Rightarrow 700 = 50\,000\,\lambda$ [1 mark] So $\lambda = 0.014\,s^{-1}$ [1 mark]

b) $T_{\frac{1}{2}} = \frac{\ln 2}{\lambda} = \frac{0.693}{0.014} = 49.5$ seconds
[2 marks available — 1 mark for the half-life equation, 1 mark for the correct half-life]

c) $N = N_0 e^{-\lambda t} = 50\,000 \times e^{-0.014 \times 300} = 750$
[2 marks available — 1 mark for the decay equation, 1 mark for the number of atoms remaining after 300 seconds]

Page 51 — Nuclear Decay

1)a) $^{226}_{88}Ra \rightarrow\ ^{222}_{86}Rn + ^{4}_{2}\alpha$ [3 marks available — 1 mark for alpha particle, 1 mark each for proton and nucleon number of radon]

b) $^{40}_{19}K \rightarrow\ ^{40}_{20}Ca + ^{0}_{-1}\beta$ [3 marks available — 1 mark for beta particle, 1 mark each for proton and nucleon number of calcium]

2) Mass defect = $(6.695 \times 10^{-27}) - (6.645 \times 10^{-27}) = 5.0 \times 10^{-29}$ kg [1 mark]. Using the equation $E = mc^2$ [1 mark], $E = (5.0 \times 10^{-29}) \times (3 \times 10^8)^2 = 4.5 \times 10^{-12}$ J [1 mark]

Page 53 — Classification of Particles

1) Proton, electron and electron antineutrino. [1 mark]
The electron and the electron antineutrino are leptons. [1 mark]
Leptons are not affected by the strong interaction, so the decay can't be due to the strong interaction. [1 mark]

2) Mesons are hadrons but the muon is a lepton. [1 mark]
The muon is a fundamental particle but mesons are not.
Mesons are built up from simpler particles. [1 mark]
Mesons feel the strong interaction but the muon does not. [1 mark]

Page 55 — Antiparticles

1) $e^+ + e^- \rightarrow \gamma + \gamma$ [1 mark]. This is called annihilation [1 mark].

2) The protons, neutrons and electrons which make up the iron atoms would need to annihilate with their antiparticles [1 mark]. No antiparticles are available in the iron block [1 mark].

3) The creation of a particle of matter requires the creation of its antiparticle. In this case no antineutron has been produced [1 mark]. Also note that the total baryon number would have increased from 2 to 3 and that's not allowed.

Page 57 — Quarks

1) uud

2) $\pi^- = d\bar{u}$ [1 mark]
Charge of down quark = –1/3 unit.
Charge of anti-up quark = –2/3 unit
Total charge = –1 unit [1 mark]

3) The weak interaction converts a down quark into an up quark plus an electron and an electron antineutrino. [1 mark]
The neutron (udd) becomes a proton (uud). [1 mark]

4) The baryon number changes from 2 to 1 so baryon number is not conserved [1 mark]. The strangeness changes from 0 to 1 so strangeness is not conserved [1 mark].

Page 59 — Binding Energy

1)a) There are 6 protons and 8 neutrons, so the mass of individual parts = $(6 \times 1.007276) + (8 \times 1.008665) = 14.112976$ u [1 mark]
Mass of $^{14}_{6}C$ nucleus = 13.999948 u
so, mass defect = 14.112976 – 13.999948 = 0.113028 u [1 mark]
Converting this into kg gives mass defect = 1.88×10^{-28} kg [1 mark]

b) $E = mc^2 = (1.88 \times 10^{-28}) \times (3 \times 10^8)^2 = 1.69 \times 10^{-11}$ J [1 mark]
1 MeV = 1.6×10^{-13} J, so energy = $\frac{1.69 \times 10^{-11}}{1.6 \times 10^{-13}} = 106$ MeV [1 mark]

2)a) Fusion [1 mark]

b) The increase in binding energy per nucleon is about 0.86 MeV [1 mark]. There are 2 nucleons in ^2H, so the increase in binding energy is about 1.72 MeV — so about 1.7 MeV is released (ignoring the positron) [1 mark].

Page 61 — Nuclear Fission and Fusion

1)a) Nuclear fission can be induced by neutrons and produces more neutrons during the process [1 mark]. This means that each fission reaction induces more fission reactions to occur, resulting in a ongoing chain of reactions [1 mark].

b) For example, control rods limit the rate of fission by absorbing neutrons [1 mark]. The number of neutrons absorbed by the rods is controlled by varying the amount they are inserted into the reactor [1 mark]. A suitable material for the control rods is boron [1 mark].

c) In an emergency shut-down, the control rods are released into the reactor [1 mark]. The control rods absorb the neutrons, and stop the reaction as quickly as possible [1 mark].

2) Advantages: keeping the reaction in the nuclear reactor going doesn't produce any waste gases that could be harmful to the environment, e.g. sulfur dioxide (leading to acid rain) or carbon dioxide [1 mark]. It can be used to supply a continuous supply of electricity, unlike some renewable sources [1 mark].
Disadvantages (any two of): problems with the reactor getting out of control / risks of radiation from radioactive waste produced / the emissions released in the case of an accident / the long half life of nuclear waste.
[1 mark for each disadvantage, maximum 2 marks]

Unit 5: Section 4 — Medical Imaging
Page 63 — X-Ray Imaging

1)a) Half-value thickness is the thickness of material required to reduce the intensity of an X-ray beam to half its original value [1 mark].

b) $\mu = \frac{\ln 2}{x_{\frac{1}{2}}} = \frac{\ln 2}{3} = 0.23\,mm^{-1}$ [1 mark], $I = I_0 e^{-\mu x} \Rightarrow \frac{I}{I_0} = e^{-\mu x}$ [1 mark].
So, $0.01 = e^{-0.23x} \Rightarrow \ln(0.01) = -0.23x$ [1 mark], $x = 20$mm [1 mark].

Page 65 — Ultrasound Imaging

1)a) $\alpha = \left(\frac{Z_{tissue} - Z_{air}}{Z_{tissue} + Z_{air}}\right)^2 = \left(\frac{1630 - 0.430}{1630 + 0.430}\right)^2$ [1 mark], $\alpha = 0.999$ [1 mark]

b) From part a), 0.1% enters the body when no gel is used [1 mark].
$\alpha = \left(\frac{Z_{tissue} - Z_{gel}}{Z_{tissue} + Z_{gel}}\right)^2 = \left(\frac{1630 - 1500}{1630 + 1500}\right)^2 = 0.002$ [1 mark], so 99.8% of the ultrasound is transmitted [1 mark]. Ratio is ~1000 [1 mark].

2)a) $Z = \rho v$ [1 mark], $v = (1.63 \times 10^6)/(1.09 \times 10^3)$
= 1495 $ms^{-1} \approx 1.50$ kms^{-1} [1 mark]

b) A pulse from the far side of the head travels an extra $2d$ cm, where d is the diameter of the head [1 mark].
Time taken to travel this distance = $2.4 \times 50 = 120\ \mu s$ [1 mark].
Distance = speed × time, so $2d = 1500 \times 120 \times 10^{-6}$
= 0.18 m [1 mark]. So $d = 9$ cm [1 mark].

84

Answers

Page 67 — Magnetic Resonance Imaging

1) a)

The axis of rotation of a spinning object [1 mark] describes a circular path around the field line [1 mark].

b) The Larmor frequency is the frequency at which the protons, or other particles, in a magnetic field precess [1 mark]. In an MRI scanner it is typically $10^3 - 10^9$ Hz [1 mark].

2) The patient lies in the centre of a large magnet, which produces a magnetic field [1 mark]. The magnetic field aligns hydrogen protons in the patient's body [1 mark]. Radio frequency coils are used to transmit radio waves, which cause the aligned protons to absorb energy [1 mark]. When the radio waves stop the protons emit the stored energy as radio waves, which are recorded by the scanner [1 mark]. A computer analyses the received radio waves to produce an image of the patient's body [1 mark].

3) Advantages, e.g. no known side effects / doesn't use ionising radiation / an image can be made for any slice in any orientation of the body / images of soft tissues are higher quality than using other techniques (e.g. CT, X-ray) / contrast can be weighted to investigate different situations.
Disadvantages, e.g. other techniques give better quality images of bony structures / people can suffer claustrophobia inside the scanner / MRI cannot be used on people with pacemakers/some metal implants / MRI scanners are very expensive.
[1 mark for each advantage explained, to a maximum of 3 marks. 1 mark for each disadvantage explained, to a maximum of 3 marks. 6 marks are available in total.]

Page 69 — Medical Uses of Nuclear Radiation

1) The patient is injected with a medical tracer consisting of a gamma source/positron-emitter bound to a substance used by the body [1 mark]. After a period of time, the radiation in the patient's body is recorded using a gamma camera/PET scanner [1 mark]. A computer uses this information to form an image, which might show a tumour as an area of high metabolic activity [1 mark].

2) a) The ionising energy of the particles released in 1000 s will be:
$1000 \times 3 \times 10^{10} \times 8 \times 10^{-13} = 24$ J [1 mark]
Absorbed dose = ionising energy ÷ mass = 24 ÷ 70 = 0.34 Gy [1 mark]

b) The effective dose of this absorbed dose is: H = 0.343 × 20 = 6.9 Sv [1 mark]

Unit 5: Section 5 — Modelling the Universe
Page 71 — The Solar System & Astronomical Distances

1) [1 mark each for 5 sensible points], e.g., planets are generally much bigger than comets. Planets are made out of rock and gas whereas comets are largely made of frozen substances like ice. Planets have almost circular orbits whereas comets have highly elliptical orbits. Comets have tails when they are close to the Sun. Comets can take millions of years to orbit the Sun; planets have much shorter periods.

2) a) A light-year is the distance travelled by a photon of light through a vacuum in one year [1 mark].

b) Seconds in a year = 365.25 × 24 × 60 × 60 = 3.16 × 10⁷ s [1 mark].
Distance = **c** × time = 3.0 × 10⁸ × 3.16 × 10⁷ = 9.5 × 10¹⁵ m [1 mark].

c) To see something, light must reach us. Light travels at a finite speed, so it takes time for that to happen [1 mark]. The further out we see, the further back in time we're looking. The Universe is ~14 billion years old so we can't see further than ~14 billion light years. [1 mark]

Page 73 — Stellar Evolution

1) High mass stars spend much less time on the main sequence than low mass stars [1 mark]. As a red giant, low mass stars can only fuse hydrogen and/or helium but the highest mass stars can fuse nuclei up to iron [1 mark]. Lower mass stars eject their atmospheres to become white dwarfs [1 mark], but high mass stars explode in supernovae [1 mark] to leave neutron stars [1 mark] or black holes [1 mark].

Page 75 — The Big Bang Model of the Universe

1) a) **v** = **H₀d** [1 mark] where **v** is recessional velocity (in kms⁻¹), **d** is distance (in Mpc) and **H₀** is Hubble's constant (in kms⁻¹Mpc⁻¹) [1 mark]

b) Hubble's law suggests that the Universe originated with the Big Bang [1 mark] and has been expanding ever since. [1 mark]

c) i) **H₀** = **v** ÷ **d** = 50 kms⁻¹ ÷ 1 Mpc⁻¹.
50 kms⁻¹ = 50 × 10³ ms⁻¹ and 1 Mpc = 3.09 × 10²² m
So, H₀ = 50 × 10³ ms⁻¹ ÷ 3.09 × 10²² m = 1.62 × 10⁻¹⁸ s⁻¹
[1 mark for the correct value, 1 mark for the correct unit]

ii) t = 1/**H₀** [1 mark]
t = 1/1.62 × 10⁻¹⁸ = 6.18 × 10¹⁷ s ≈ 20 billion years [1 mark]
The observable Universe has a radius of 20 billion light years. [1 mark]

2) a) **z** ≈ **v**/c [1 mark] so **v** ≈ 0.37 × 3.0 × 10⁸ ≈ 1.1 × 10⁸ ms⁻¹ [1 mark]

b) **d** = **v**/H₀ ≈ 1.1 × 10⁸ / 2.4 × 10⁻¹⁸ = 4.6 × 10²⁵ m [1 mark]
= 4.6 × 10²⁵ / 9.5 × 10¹⁵ ly = 4.9 billion ly [1 mark]

3) The cosmic background radiation is microwave radiation [1 mark] showing a continuous spectrum [1 mark] of a temperature of about 3 K [1 mark]. It is isotropic and homogeneous [1 mark].
It suggests that the ancient Universe was very hot, producing lots of electromagnetic radiation [1 mark] and that its expansion has stretched the radiation into the microwave region [1 mark].
[1 mark for clearly linking the evidence to the explanation.]

Page 77 — Evolution of the Universe

1) a) The amount of curvature of the Universe depends on its average density [1 mark]. Current estimates for the density of the Universe are close to the critical density required for the Universe to be flat [1 mark].

b) A flat Universe can be modelled by a 2-dimensional plane where parallel lines never meet and the angles in a triangle add up to 180° [1 mark]. In a **flat** Universe, gravity is **just strong enough** to stop the expansion at **t** = ∞ [1 mark], which means that the Universe will expand for ever, but more and more slowly with time [1 mark].

2) a) Find **H₀** in SI units: **H₀** = 100 kms⁻¹Mpc⁻¹
So, **H₀** = 100 × 10³ ÷ 3.09 × 10²² = 3.236 × 10⁻¹⁸ s⁻¹ [1 mark]

Find the average density using: $\rho_0 = \dfrac{3H_0{}^2}{8\pi G}$ [1 mark]
and G = 6.67 × 10⁻¹¹ Nm²kg⁻² [1 mark].

$\rho_0 = \dfrac{3 \times \left(3.236 \times 10^{-18}\right)^2}{8 \times \pi \times 6.67 \times 10^{-11}} = 1.87 \times 10^{-26}$ kgm⁻³ [1 mark]

b) The average density of the Universe is 1.87 × 10⁻²⁶ kgm⁻³, so on average, each m³ of the Universe has a mass of 1.87 × 10⁻²⁶ kg [1 mark].
This is equivalent to 1.87 × 10⁻²⁶ ÷ 1.7 × 10⁻²⁷ = 11 hydrogen atoms. So there would be 11 hydrogen atoms in every m³ if the entire mass of the Universe was hydrogen [1 mark].

3) A slight excess of matter was produced over antimatter [1 mark]. The matter and antimatter annihilated into photons [1 mark]. The remaining matter was in the form of quarks and leptons [1 mark]. As the Universe expanded and cooled the quarks combined to form particles like protons and neutrons [1 mark]. Some of the protons fused together to form helium [1 mark]. After about 300 000 years the Universe was cool enough for electrons to combine with the protons and helium nuclei to form atoms [1 mark]. The Universe became transparent since the photons could no longer interact with any free charges [1 mark]. There were fluctuations in the density of the Universe [1 mark] that allowed gravity to clump matter together, condensing matter into stars and galaxies [1 mark]. [1 mark for a clear, logical progression of ideas in the answer.]

x

Index

Index